THE EFFECT OF SOCIAL MEDIA ON ADOLESCENTS' MENTAL HEALTH AND WELL-BEING

THE EFFECT OF SOCIAL MEDIA ON ADOLESCENTS' MENTAL HEALTH AND WELL-BEING

Dr Steph Adam

Matador
9 Priory Business Park,
Wistow Road, Kibworth Beauchamp,
Leicestershire. LE8 0RX
Tel: 0116 279 2299
Email: books@troubador.co.uk
Web: www.troubador.co.uk/matador
Twitter: @matadorbooks

ISBN 978 1 8004 6510 7

British Library Cataloguing in Publication Data.
A catalogue record for this book is available from the British Library.

Printed and bound by CPI Group (UK) Ltd, Croydon, CR0 4YY
Typeset in 11pt Adobe Garamond Pro by Troubador Publishing Ltd, Leicester, UK

Matador is an imprint of Troubador Publishing Ltd

For Charlie Adam aged 17, Riley Adam aged 12,
Freddy Schiewe aged 12 and Oscar Hight aged 8.
You have all unwittingly contributed to the making of this book.

CONTENTS

PREFACE

Three years ago, while walking my nine-year-old grandsons, Riley and Freddy, to school, I saw a large crowd of adolescents approaching the crossroads, chatting, not to each other, but on their mobile phones. Most of them had their mobiles glued to their ears and continued to cross the road without looking to see if there was anything coming. This group seemed to be more interested in engaging with someone they could not see, than attending to their own safety. They were responding to one feature of digital technology, their mobile phones, which have invaded their lives at home, in schools, in colleges and in external surroundings. This observation sparked an interest in me as to 'why' young people choose to engage with their peers in this way. So, I set out to investigate what the attraction is for them in using their mobiles to communicate with each other, instead of meeting up after school in the traditional way.

I was already accustomed to how young people interact with each other during their offline world during my time supporting young people through their difficulties. First as a support worker for homeless adolescents, then as a Young Person's Counsellor for secondary schools in North Yorkshire, and finally as the Lead Counsellor for a local college's student counselling service. But I did not have any experience of their online world.

When researching the phenomenon of adolescents and their use of their mobiles, I discovered they access a multitude of other online digital technologies, such as social media networking sites, video-sharing platforms and online gaming. Young people use these sites to interact with each other, post various content, and share their ideas with others. As I accumulated my research evidence, I realised that when adolescents use digital these sites, they change the way they identify with themselves, their families, their peers, and the society in which they live. This change has had a knock-on effect on their psychological well-being and developing personalities.

I will outline the benefits and risks in my publication *The Effect of Social Media on Adolescents' Mental Health and Well-Being,* as well as highlighting the main reasons why adolescents like to use digital technology. I then explain how we can help adolescents to navigate safely through this new virtual world we now live in.

This book is written primarily for parents (including adult caregivers) and teachers of young people aged 11-18 years. In this age of technology more communication is taking place online. Therefore, media education is needed, and parents and teachers should be provided with more information about adolescents' online activities. I have attempted to do this by researching this topic and writing a resource for readers to use, when teaching their adolescents about social media.

ACKNOWLEDGEMENTS

This book would not have been published without the help of many people. My thanks go to Alison Williams (alisonwilliamswriting.wordpress.com), a freelance editor, who's skilled editing made me aware of the changes required to complete my final draft. This resulted in the finished narrative being more insightful for both parents and teachers.

I wish to acknowledge and thank the work carried out by Troubador Publishing, especially Hannah Dakin who introduced me to the first stages of manuscript submission; Joshua Howey who brought to life my manuscript by overseeing the production process; Sophie Morgan managed my marketing data for a press release coupled with an advance information sheet for bookshops; Lauren Stenning who proofread the final document before it went to print; and Jack Wedgbury who designed the cover. They have all transformed my manuscript into a professional non-fiction read.

I am appreciative of the time spent by my daughters Rachael Adam and Sarah Schiewe, who patiently read many drafts and became my associates in the early days of planning the content.

I want to also thank Sarah for creating the illustrations to portray complex ideas and make them more accessible for my readers. My gratitude goes to a sister Barbara Lambert for providing an illustration of the Bobo Doll.

My thanks go to Alison Harper of Alquin Social Media in Selby, who designs and markets my Facebook and Twitter accounts. She has raised the profile of this book.

I am grateful to James McHugh (https://yorlifephotography. com) who took the photograph that is featured on the back cover.

I am very grateful to the following for allowing permission to reproduce material:

Joseph-Salsibury, R. (2020) *Race and Racism in English Secondary Schools.* Runnymede: London, pp. 61–62.
YMCA (2020) *Young discriminated and Black: the true colour of institutional racism in the UK.* https://www.ymca.org.uk, pp. 62–63.

TABLES AND FIGURES

1

A NEW ERA OF DIGITAL NATIVES

Many of the older generation, including me, do not have a compass to guide us through this new technological world we now live in. We cannot turn to people in the same age group for advice, as most of us grew up in an age without social media (before 1980) and mobile phones were not used for social reasons. As adults we may have stumbled into this digital space knowing that we should try and get used to it. It is changing everything we do, from our working life to our shopping, and even socialising with family and friends.

Digital Immigrants vs. Digital Natives

Marc Prensky (2001), a consultant and designer in education, invented the concept of 'Digital Immigrants' and 'Digital Natives' to understand the gap between the youth of today and the way in which people who do not know anything about technology learn about knowledge. He claims that people who were raised before technology existed may have some idea of the internet, and social media. But, in the same way that someone learning a foreign language will retain some of their original accent, we, the older generation he calls Digital Immigrants, follow suit, by clinging onto our past way of learning (Prensky, 2001).

Prensky (2001) also says that the introduction of digital technology has made pupils and students think differently and using outdated teaching methods will make it difficult for them to achieve academically. Adolescents who are part of this group are called Digital Natives because they are raised in a digital world and need a media rich environment to focus on, as they do not know anything different. It is difficult to know when, exactly, the division started between the two groups, as Prensky does not explicitly say, but it is generally attached to age. In the context of this book the term Digital Natives applies to anyone born after 1980.

So, are we left with the Digital Immigrants who might be considered by the Digital Natives as relics of the past, while the latter group evolve into the globe's dominant, knowing population? This cultural divide makes it challenging for parents and teachers to know how to approach the problems associated with social media. My research question starts with "How can parents and teachers create a safe, digital environment where our young people can learn and grow, but at the same time protect them from the dangers that this new type of technology may bring?"

To begin, I will explain what I consider to be one of the main reasons this cultural division is causing so many problems. I have had discussions with my 17-year-old grandson Charlie and his friends about this, and they informed me they use online social media primarily to communicate with their peers. This is in line with previous research (Subrahmanyam et al., 2001) showing how social networking sites such as Facebook,

Twitter, Snapchat, YouTube, Myspace, Instagram and, more recently, TikTok have transformed the way in which adolescents communicate with each other. These sites are becoming more widely used and are replacing face-to-face interactions with online exchanges (Boyd & Ellison, 2007).

Mobile Phones and Self-Presentation

Communication between peers is achieved primarily with their mobile phones as they are more accessible than laptops and provide greater opportunities for online self-presentation. Self-presentation can be defined as the act of giving accurate or inaccurate information regarding oneself to others (Leary, 1995). When adolescents take part in self-presentation, they usually present different aspects of themselves to others that matter to them. Therefore, visual self-presentation by this age group is clearly directed at managing the impressions made on others and gaining acceptance by their peer group. When describing online self-presentation throughout the book, I will be relating it to profile pictures as they are considered by researchers to be the most important tool for self-presentation on social media sites (Strano, 2008).

While photos traditionally functioned as mementoes for birthdays or weddings, today's youth take 'selfies', i.e. one's own or group photos taken with a mobile phone. A combination of the front-facing camera and the possibility of sharing these images online have now turned selfies into a mainstream cultural practice. Adolescents create accounts on different social media sites and update their online profiles by uploading a photo of themselves, where multiple options are provided to respond to each other. These sites are easily accessible by young people using their mobiles at the click of a button. While on these sites, thoughts, photos, videos, favourite music and movies are shared (Manago et al., 2008), as well as other content about social lives which can reach a vast audience of friends, relatives, acquaintances and sometimes strangers (Lee-Won et al., 2014).

Here lies one of the important differences between Digital Immigrants and Digital Natives. This user-generated communication about content differs from traditional face-to-face communication and interaction that I and other Digital Immigrants are accustomed to. That is because there is no eye contact, no tone of voice, and spontaneous facial expressions and auditory cues are missing. One of the reasons young people communicate in this way is the fact that they have grown up accepting this is normal behaviour, and they can maintain relationships twenty-four hours a day if they choose to do so.

Why Collecting 'Likes' Is Important

Young people are continually using their mobile phones to check their posts on sites such as Facebook to find out, "How many 'likes' did my post get?" The word 'like' in this context refers to a positive response from other people who have seen the post, and sites have built-in mechanisms to express a range of emotions to such content. Consequently, adolescents can form their own impression of a post or video, but they can also see how many others, and often exactly who, has expressed approval. Conformity to peer norms is generally rewarded with peer validation expressed by the number of 'likes', which are then equated to a marker of one's popularity.

Therefore, some adolescents post images on social media to gain rewards or to claim a favourable identity for themselves, because these sites enable them to self-disclose to a broad and anonymous audience. The aim of self-presentation is to achieve a high number of 'likes' on their social media sites, thus fulfilling their need for public acknowledgement (Jang et al., 2015). This was echoed by a large-scale investigation carried out by Cable News Network (Hadid, 2015, cited by Benn, 2017) into the use of various social media sites by adolescents aged thirteen. The researchers analysed what these young people say to each other, and why they check their messages up to a hundred times a day. Their responses are summarised below:

Table 1.0 Reasons Young People Use Social Media

Reason	%
To see if their posts are collecting 'likes' or comments	61
To check if their friends are doing things without them	36
To make sure no one was saying mean things about them	21

The researchers found that the group of adolescents were anxious, largely due to a need to protect their popularity status, and to oppose those who challenge it (Hadid, 2015). It is concerning that such a high number of this group were worried about collecting 'likes.' For those who did not get a high number, this may potentially affect their self-esteem through paying so much attention to peer approval. The young people who responded by saying they were checking to see if their friends were doing things without them, could have been experiencing a type of worry called a fear of missing out (FoMO) (Davis, 2012). This is a psychological trait which is described as apprehension, or social anxiety that others may be enjoying social events or other rewarding experiences from which one is absent (Wang et al., 2018). It has been noted that young people with high levels of FoMO are sensitive about their social bonds and have a desire to stay continually connected with what others are doing (Przybylski et al., 2013). The results also show that some participants are concerned about how they fit in with their peer group. This need is true for most adolescents, but the dangers of online derogatory comments could also affect their self-esteem and confidence levels.

There are some benefits for young people having mobile phones. In an investigation into adolescents and their parents, researchers found that all the parents viewed mobiles as important for keeping in touch, and in monitoring their young peoples' safety (Devitt & Roker, 2009). However, some of the adolescents thought there were several risks, including withdrawing into their own world, and having a false sense of security by possessing a mobile phone (Devitt & Roker, 2009). I believe it is tempting for shy adolescents or those who do not appear confident to retreat into an 'unreal' world and stay there, where they feel most comfortable.

Social Media and Adolescents' Mental Health

A review into adolescents' mental health claimed that one in three British 15-year-olds use social media sites extensively for up to six hours a day (Education Policy Institute, 2017) and most sites have a minimum age limit of thirteen. When discussing adolescents' mental health, we need to consider that these years are a turbulent time for their development because of the dramatic changes which take place, including changes to their bodies, advanced understanding, and changing social expectations. The combination of these changes makes it a demanding time and some adolescents may succumb to mental health issues at some point during this phase of their development. Mental health difficulties among young people such as anxiety and depression have increased by 70 per cent in the past twenty-five years. However, this increase could be because professionals are highlighting mental health problems much earlier than two decades ago, where previously it may have gone unnoticed. But I believe that this does not account solely for the increase. The use of social media amongst adolescents causes some parents, teachers, and mental health practitioners to question whether the use of these sites is proving harmful to young people.

For example, in a report published by the Royal Society of Public Health (RSPH, 2017) in conjunction with the Young Health Movement (YHM), researchers claimed the use of social media is more addictive than alcohol or cigarettes. Being addicted to social media is not recognised as a disorder by the psychiatric community and was not included in the recently released Diagnostic and Statistical Manual of Mental Disorder V (DSM-V), published by the American Psychiatric Association. Young people seem especially vulnerable, with case studies highlighting students whose academic performance decreases as they spend more and more time online. Some students also suffer health-related issues caused by a lack of sleep, as they stay up late to chat online, check for social network status updates or to try to reach the next level in a game (Wallace, 2014).

The same researchers who published the earlier report (YHM) also include a list of five of the popular social media sites according to their impact on adolescents' well-being in the UK. They are as follows: (1) YouTube is the most positive as some of the videos can raise awareness about a particular problem. One risk is there are sometimes inappropriate videos without warning, for instance showing adolescents being violent; (2) Twitter is used for social messaging. Another risk is there are false profiles displayed; (3) Facebook can match adolescents with other users and help to build up friendships. However, predators have targeted young people on this site. It can also encourage cyberbullying, and there may be unsuitable content displayed; (4) Snapchat allows adolescents to send videos and photos called 'snaps' to friends which disappear after ten seconds and become inaccessible. One risk is when someone sends a snap it is extremely easy for others to screenshot it. This means they may have the original snap on their camera for ever; (5) Instagram was the worst platform as it consists entirely of user-generated photographs which are largely airbrushed. It generates an unnecessary system of one-upmanship creating a sense of failure in young people before their early lives have even begun.

A recent *Panorama* documentary on Netflix enquired 'Is TikTok Safe?' This site is described as one of the fastest growing social media networking sites of all time. It is used by young people as an outlet to share short videos expressing themselves, for example through singing and dancing. Although users of the site should be more than thirteen years old, in a report for the BBC current affairs show, *Panorama*, reporter Tina Daheley claimed anyone can put in a fictitious birthday to create an account. Daheley found that when she opened an account, she received a host of different content that she had not asked for.

For the purposes of this investigation, a 23-year-old woman created an account as a 14-year-old and used hashtags such as 'school life' to indicate she was attending school. Her TikTok account was soon followed by several older men with a 34-year-old sending her explicit sexual messages even when she told him she was only fourteen years of age. However, despite this content being flagged by other users, TikTok only acted four days after *Panorama* contacted them. TikTok uses an algorithm to make suggestions of up to sixty-second clips, based on user interactions, such as the videos a user likes or shares, accounts they follow, and comments posted, as well as their hashtags. So, if an adolescent is watching sexual dance moves, TikTok will send more videos with similar sexual dancing which could then be viewed by potential predators who know where to look for these images.

Whilst it is important to recognise the problems that come with social media, it would be remiss of me to ignore the benefits which have been reported, which include increased self-esteem, perceived social support from chatting to others with similar problems, and an increased opportunity for self-disclosure, which results in a sense of belonging to a group (Davis, 2012). Above all, adolescents who find it difficult to interact with peers in face-to-face environments can benefit from their online communication and make new friends. All these online activities involve higher order thought processes and reasonable language and literacy skills, which will prove beneficial in later life.

—

To maintain positive friendships, individuals need to show compassion and kindness which cannot be learnt quickly and if adolescents are devoid of these skills this can lead to individual and collective unrest in our communities. Digital technology is an important social project and one that affects all of us. However, current research does not always reach the people who matter, i.e. you, the readers. Therefore, I have used both in-depth studies and large-scale investigations from researchers in different countries to understand how social media is affecting adolescents' identities, personalities, mental health, and well-being. I do not claim these studies are right or wrong. Instead, they are used to raise an awareness of mental health issues taking place amongst our young people. As a former counsellor, I was already aware that the nature and causes of mental health issues were changing rapidly and increasing amongst adolescents since I retired in 2011.

In the next chapter I describe how young peoples' identities and personalities are influenced by genetics, parents, and other important people in their lives as well as the cultural context in which they are raised. But their identities and personalities are changing all the time because they are now incorporating social media sites into their everyday lives. In subsequent chapters I consider the effects that social media is having on them with reference to: bullying and cyberbullying; body image; offline and online racism; sexual orientations; posting and viewing sexual material and sexting; alcohol references and adolescent consumption; self-harm and suicide; and playing video games. In the final chapter I summarise the benefits and risks for young people using digital technology, along with an account of my own learning. I have also recorded a list of resources for readers to access within the chapters, as well as a reference list for further reading.

2

THE DEVELOPMENT OF
IDENTITY AND PERSONALITY

The development of identity is defined as an internal, continuous subjective view of ourselves as individuals (Reber & Reber, 2001). It consists of the beliefs, ideals and values that go towards making us into unique human beings. Identity is only part of the process that makes us who we are. There are also our developing personalities which are influenced by hereditary characteristics, influences from significant others, as well as our cultural contexts in which we live in. In this chapter I will describe one theory of identity development, and this will be followed by an explanation of how our personalities are formed. Finally, I will clarify how adolescents' identities and personalities are changing from pre-social media to post-social media, along with different ways of building friendships.

Stages of Identity Development

Erik Erikson (1995), one of the best-known theorists of identity, claimed that identity constantly changes due to new experiences and information that individuals acquire in their daily interaction with others. When people have new experiences, they also take on new challenges which can help or hinder the development of identity. Erikson (1995) stated that identity development consists of a navigation through eight stages from birth to old age, (see appendix A for a detailed summary of these stages). In each stage, Erikson (1995) believed people experience a psychological tension that serves as a turning point in their development. If individuals successfully deal with this tension, they will feel a sense of mastery and emerge from each stage with psychological strengths that will serve them well for the rest of their lives. If they fail to deal effectively with the conflict, they may not develop the essential skills needed for a strong sense of self.

According to Erikson (1995), during stage five, that is, between 12–18 years of age, adolescents search for a sense of self and personal identity, through an exploration of personal values, beliefs, and goals. This is a major phase of development where young people will continually re-examine their identities and try to find out exactly who they are. Adolescents, while negotiating social interactions and 'fitting in', must at the same time develop a sense of morality and learn right from wrong. Young people also ask questions during this stage, for example, "Who am I and how do I fit into the world around me?" Answers to these questions are important since a positive sense of identity has been linked to psychological well-being such as increased confidence and high self-esteem (Beronsky, 2003). Failing to establish a sense of identity can lead to role confusion where adolescents are not sure about themselves or their place in society. However, those who successfully get through this stage will have the ability to continuously explore their identity, while still being able to commit to accepting others, even when there may be cultural differences. One major weakness of Erikson's (1995) theory is that the exact mechanisms for resolving conflict and moving from one stage to the next are not adequately described. However, his theory does provide a broad framework from which to view the development of identity throughout the entire lifespan.

The Development of Personality

The development of personality also needs to be considered alongside the concept of how identity is constructed. Defining personality is a slippery concept as there are several theories, and it depends on which theory one favours. I will use the 'nature versus nurture' debate which claims there are two opposing views that influence personality development. To keep things simple, I have used equal scales to represent the causes of this debate.

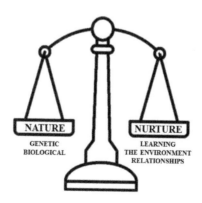

Fig. 2.0 Personality Pre-Social Media.
Illustration by Sarah Schiewe.

The illustration shows how personality is formed before the advent of social media and it shows the two causes.

Nature

The nature view states that personality is the cause of genetic inheritance and other biological factors. Hereditary factors are based on the knowledge that people who are closely related share more genes. For example, as well as resembling my mother facially I am blessed with her creative streak (she was an artist), but my creativity is expressed in words instead of artistic form. There is also biological basis for personality development, which is related to the brain function and patterns of neurotransmitter activity. For myself, after having a stroke (from which I fortunately recovered), my brain has rewired itself, and family members have observed that I am more emotional than I was before I had my stroke.

Nurture

Those who favour the nurture influence claim that at birth, human minds are like blank slates that are gradually filled with the process of learning, the degree of stimulation in the environment, relationships with others, and the cultural context in which one is raised. I was brought up in a RAF environment, and as a child moved home every two years. This influenced me to change my jobs and my choice of houses frequently as an adult, and this has resulted in me being perceived as impulsive by friends and close family members.

Personality change

Personality can be characterised by how others perceive us (funny, kind, grumpy) and that may be different to how we see ourselves. I am reminded of how Scrooge's personality changed in *A Christmas Carol* (Dickens, 2018), a novel about a mean-spirited, selfish old man, who hates Christmas. One Christmas Eve, Scrooge is unkind to Bob Cratchit who works for him, refuses to give to charity, and is rude to his nephew Fred when he invites Scrooge to spend Christmas with him.

That evening Scrooge is visited by a series of spirits called the Ghosts of Christmas Past, Christmas Present and Christmas Yet to Come. They show Scrooge how his mean behaviour has affected those around him. The ghosts' journeys teach Scrooge the error of his ways. When he wakes up on Christmas Day, he is relieved to discover that there is still time for him to change, and he is now transformed into a generous human being. Scrooge buys the biggest turkey for the Cratchit family before spending the day with his nephew, thus embodying the spirit of Christmas. Although Dickens' novel is fictitious, it does serve to illustrate how one's personality can change when confronted with external influences.

The effect of social media on the nature vs. nurture debate

I will demonstrate how, by adding social media into the nurture side of this debate, it increases the way that an individual's behaviour is pulled unconsciously to this side of the personality scale.

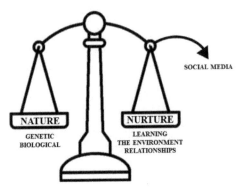

Fig. 2.1 Personality Post-Social Media.
Illustration by Sarah Schiewe.

When an offshoot of social media is added to the nurture side of the scales it could be beneficial if the fallout from this new arm was filled with positive learning and experiences. However, that is not always the case. We shall see in the following chapters how many young people are so preoccupied with social media, they acquire their sense of self-worth by communicating through their online selves, by trying to become more popular with their peers. This ultimately affects how adolescents behave towards others. The ongoing debate regarding nature versus nurture is concerned with the contribution that both sides have towards human behaviour, particularly concerning how individuals relate to other people.

Behaviour in Everyday Life

Erving Goffman's book *The Presentation of Self in Everyday Life* (1990), had a significant impact on the sociological understanding of face-to-face interactions. Goffman (1990) claims that people behave like actors on a stage, and describes how, while in the presence of others, individuals engage in ongoing self-presentation aimed at making impressions on others. Presentation of the self in everyday life is about the practice of 'impression management' (an important aspect of avoiding being seen in unflattering ways) and involves learning how people interact with others, and to maintain control of the situation by putting on a 'face' (Goffman, 1990).

Goffman states that people emphasise the importance of the social setting in which they perform their actions, and these actions are influenced by an audience (Goffman, 1990). He makes an important distinction between front-stage behaviour, when actions are visible to an audience, and back-stage performances which occur when no audience is present.

Front-stage performance

A front-stage performance is shaped by public social norms, and, whatever the setting, individuals are aware of how others perceive them and what they expect. This knowledge informs them of how to behave in future interactions. For example, a young man who is a waiter who wants to keep his job will ensure that he dresses appropriately and behaves in a courteous manner to his customers when waiting on them at a table. The downside of this type of behaviour is that those individuals who spend so long in front-stage performances, trying their best to give off a certain impression to others, can hide their true self, or, worse still, eliminate any sense of self.

Back-stage performance

Individuals use a back-stage performance when they feel free from the expectations that influence their behaviour when they are on the front-stage. Take the same waiter who has just served his customers. On entering the kitchen, he reverts to being more casual and may do things that customers would frown upon, for example, tasting food using his fingers from several plates which are being prepared for his next customers. The benefit of being back-stage is that individuals are often more relaxed and become closer to their real characteristics and traits, and thus behave more informally.

—

Although the two examples of front-stage and back-stage behaviour may seem a bit extreme, they do serve to differentiate between the two types. When a performance typically reserved for one area makes its way into another, confusion can happen. For this reason, most people perhaps unconsciously try hard to make sure that these two realms remain separate from each other.

Online Identity

I will use Goffman's (1990) theory throughout this section of the chapter to explain the formation of online identity. Young people have incorporated selfies into the process of exploring their identity online through the means of their self-presentation. When adolescents are posting photos and messages, I believe many of them are behaving from a front-stage performance perspective (sometimes sub-consciously) where their audience may include their entire social media community. During their back-stage performance, their audience will consist of family and close friends, where they can express characteristics that were previously out of sight.

But for others, who may not be sure who their audiences are, this makes it more problematic for individuals to manage the boundaries between the two domains (Marwick & Boyd, 2011). When an audience is not entirely known, individuals rely on the mental image of the people with whom they are communicating to inform their thoughts and behaviour (Litt, 2012). This concept is known as an 'imaginary audience' and it has long influenced people's thoughts and actions during everyday writing and speaking (Litt, 2012). But today, when incorporating social media into their lives, individuals need to navigate through public spaces with potentially large and invisible audiences. Researchers have begun to question who people perceive as their audience as they perform in these public spaces (Litt, 2012). In the case of adolescents, this may lead them unintentionally to not just sharing their posts to a few of their friends, but also to an audience of hundreds of people. This can result in the possibility of receiving many different types of responses. For example, they could receive favourable comments from peers, but critical comments from adults, and this difference may lead to confusion, particularly with younger adolescents.

Different online identities

Social media can provide many opportunities to explore different aspects of the self. Individuals may edit and manipulate certain features of their physical photos to make themselves appear more attractive. And the autonomy of social media may make some people feel more confident about disclosing certain aspects of their self, because of a lack of opportunity to disclose these features in real life.

Research carried out by Zhao et al., (2008) focussed on how online identities are constructed by students using Facebook. The researchers noted that some of the students constructed an account for the public to be seen by everyone, but others created accounts for friends with the public blocked from viewing. There were many different online photos that were used by this group; some were carefully edited while others were quite plain (Zhao et al., 2008). Despite the levels of sophistication, all the participants attempted to depict a socially attractive self. Many of this group were happy to let the public see a wide range of photos portraying themselves with their peers, having fun, and showing affection towards each other. One claim that was made by many of the students was that they were trying to be more popular with their friends (Zhao et al., 2008). Regarding individual profile photos, most users decided not to show their faces at all, or to show their faces along with others, which suggests an attempt to form a 'group-orientated identity' (Zhao et al., 2008).

The results showed that these students produced three different types of online Facebook identities. The 'real self' consists of the way in which individuals present themselves in face-to-face interactions. Social media also provides opportunities that encourage individuals to reveal their 'true self', including aspects which were previously hidden in face-to-face encounters. For the first time, individuals can publicly express their 'hoped-for possible selves', which empowers people to actualise the identities they hope to establish but are unable to do in face-to-face interactions. For example, a boy may wish to become a famous footballer, but lacks the opportunity to show off his skills. However, such 'hoped-for-possible selves' may not be anchored in reality, especially when individuals adapt their behaviour to conform to social expectations. For example, I have described how these students use Facebook to appear part of a group (conforming to peers' social expectations) to increase their popularity and friendships. Therefore, these students' 'hoped-for-possible selves' will be that they want to be part of a peer group. However, it becomes problematic for them if they are not accepted.

The use of Facebook creates a multi-audience identity construction site (Zhao et al., 2008). The control that users have over their privacy settings enable them to partition many 'back' and 'front' domains (Goffman, 1990), where they can stage different identity performances for a wide range of audiences. However, this may mean some people are blind to who their audiences are at any given time.

Peer Friendships

Offline friendships

Elkind (1967), a child psychologist, used the term 'imaginary audience' to describe the phenomenon where adolescents anticipate the reactions of other people in actual or impending social situations. This kind of anticipation could be explained by adolescents' preoccupation that others are as admiring or as critical of them, as they are of themselves (Elkind, 1967). As a result, an audience is created, and adolescents believe they will be the focus of attention. Elkind (1967) also believed that the construction of imaginary audiences would partially account for a wide variety of adolescent behaviours and experiences; and this imagination also plays a role in the self-consciousness that emerges in early adolescence.

For those born before 1980, friendships were formed in a traditional way through interactions at school, at college, and mixing with other adolescents who had similar hobbies. Consequently, young people's independence was increased from being influenced via parents' roles to peer groups in a more gradual way. For example, parents would meet other adolescents – their daughter or son's friends – in the settings previously described. This meant that parents had greater control over the type of friends their young people were choosing to relate to.

For many adolescents, their need to become part of a peer group becomes critical to their identity development (Brechwald & Prinstein, 2011) and exclusion from a group may impact negatively on their self-esteem, sense of belonging and emotional well-being (Berzonsky, 2003). One way to enhance their well-being is to achieve peer-group recognition by increasing their social bonds with face-to-face interactions and conforming to the standards and needs of their group. Essentially, by interacting with others and getting feedback, adolescents assess certain values that they think are important, then evaluate similarities and differences to determine how they measure up to others in their peer group.

Online friendships

To increase their offline encounters, adolescents extend their friendships by interacting with others online – this provides opportunities to seek approval and increase their network of friends. A study by Davis (2012) explored the role that social media plays in young people's experience of friendship and identity. The questions asked included, "What does social media mean to you, and how does it fit into other aspects of your lives?". Most of the participants taking part used Facebook, and instant messaging such as MSN, AOL, and Skype to communicate with their friends. Her analysis of the young people's responses show online peer communications can provide adolescents with a 'sense of belonging' and 'self-disclosure'. These are two significant features that reinforce identity development during the adolescent years (Davis, 2012).

Sense of belonging

This group reported the most common use for social media was to send messages to their friends. By communicating in this way this allowed them to have a sense of connection to each other, irrespective of where they were at the time or what time it was during the day (Davis, 2012). Whilst this activity meets the necessity of having a sense of belonging, it raises questions about the ability to achieve an independent sense of self. For example, some adolescents reached for their mobiles to eliminate feelings of boredom, because they were reluctant to have this type of experience. One girl expressed a feeling of anxiety at the thought of being electronically shut off from her friends for any length of time (Davis, 2012) which constitutes her dependency on others.

Self-disclosure

Regarding self-disclosure, the respondents were split into three age groups, 13–14, 15–16, and 17–18 years of age. The results showed that peers provide opportunities for the participants to engage in intimate exchanges that consist of personal disclosures between friends, such as asking for advice because they are experiencing a conflict. The 13–14 age group had the highest numbers of self-disclosures with 83 per cent. This result contrasts with previous research on the same topic which identified that it is older adolescents who engage in intimate online exchanges (Schouten et al., 2007).

One of the reasons for this discrepancy may be that younger participants spoke more often about intimate disclosures as these exchanges are more important and carry more weight (Davis, 2012). This is because self-disclosure is still a relatively new peer process in early adolescence development (Brown & Larson, 2009). Also, in the 1960s the desire for an adolescent's privacy and a reluctance to share information was recognised by Elkind (1967) who thought it could be a reaction to feeling under constant scrutiny by others. The remaining two categories had results which were similar with 15–16-year-olds showing 65 per cent, and the 17–18 age range reported 67 per cent (Davis, 2012). Nearly half of the young people, particularly girls and those who felt shy, said they felt it is easier to share personal disclosures online rather than in face-to-face encounters (Davis, 2012).

One girl described finding it hard to explain her emotions face-to-face with her friends as she does not want them to know how she is feeling. She therefore uses her mobile to talk to her friends, as they can help her to sort her problems out (Davis, 2012). Another girl said she has more control when using her phone because she has time to consider her words before messaging her friends. This means she can communicate her ideas more clearly (Davis, 2012).

This study shows some of the benefits that social media can bring by encouraging young people to have contact with their friends and to feel a sense of belonging with their peers. However, by sharing problems through messages, adolescents respond without a visual representation of the sender. Instead of using the body language that comes with face-to-face physical contact, all they see are words expressed on a screen. When they discuss their feelings in this way, the responses cannot live up to live facial expressions or set the context in which the original message was received. Therefore, I believe it remains a lottery as to whether any advice given is helpful.

Summary

The need to belong to a peer group plays a critical role in the lives of young people because socialising has a positive impact on human development. Social media can also guarantee the feeling of being constantly connected to one's peer group and may encourage a sense of belonging which is crucial as adolescents try to find a sense of their own identities and personalities. However, using social media can lead to an unrealistic lifestyle as some adolescents fail to identify how much of their online selves is make-believe. With the amount of peer pressure to conform to peer beliefs, a 'cloned' self could emerge through imitating others in their group, denying their true potential the chance to emerge. Furthermore, a huge influence in this potential cloning is the virtual world which caters for and can provide adolescents with the largest audiences they could ever hope for.

Young people may not be able to strike a balance between the benefits and risks that using social media can bring. I would therefore encourage you as parents to act as role models for the behaviour you would like them to express on their social media platforms. Adolescents tend to mimic behaviour, so it is important to reflect the same values and beliefs you would like them to adopt. You can achieve this by actively looking for opportunities to discuss what they post, who they share their posts with, what feedback they receive, and how they feel about any comments. Finally, encourage your son or daughter to form strong offline relationships to ensure they do not become over reliant on the approval of online relationships which may have a negative effect on their psychological health and well-being.

3

BULLYING AND CYBERBULLYING

Bullying and cyberbullying can occur directly towards targeted individuals, or in an indirect way such as spreading rumours about them. Types of bullying and cyberbullying include physical and verbal threats and efforts to harm the reputation of these people, and/or damage to their property. This type of behaviour often takes place at schools or colleges where the perception of one's peers can have a huge impact on generating adolescents' thoughts and feelings about themselves. Christine Pratt, founder of the National Bullying Helpline (www.nationalbullyinghelpline.co.uk), suggests there are several factors which make children and adolescents become vindictive towards others. She asserts that peer pressure coupled with digital technology provides platforms for young people to commit these horrible acts anonymously. Pratt also explains that young people behave in this way because they want to control someone, as they lack control in society or feel that a particular individual is a possible threat to their role.

Offline Bullying

I frequently came across offline bullying while counselling young adolescents attending North Yorkshire secondary schools and found the main reason pupils were bullied, was because they were seen by their peers to be different. The pupils I counselled told me they were considered different because they wore glasses, were overweight, or seemed unattractive. Once I had the consent of the young person to inform their parents, the parents reported the bullying to the school, and in most cases it stopped. Where the bullying did not cease, and the board of governors were involved, this invariably led to the victim or the bully leaving the school.

One of my daughters was teased at secondary school when she was about to start the second year of her GSCE subjects during the 1990s. She was bullied because a group of girls found out that I was in a relationship with a woman. She was repeatedly taunted with the words, "Your mum's a lezzie", and was excluded from group activities. Despite going through the normal complaints procedure and eventually reporting the bullies to the board of governors, the bullies were not reprimanded. Because rules around bullying were complacent in the 1990s and the bullying did not stop, I removed my daughter from the school. I subsequently enrolled myself and her at a local college so that I could teach her the GSCE subjects myself. We both passed five subjects each and that was enough for both of us to carve out successful future careers.

In my last job as lead counsellor at a local college, most of the students who came for counselling were young girls. They were constantly bullied by other girls, often in groups, and told they were fat, or ugly. Others who were bullied included adolescents who were identified as being in the lesbian, gay, bisexual, or transgender group, or those who had mental health issues. Whilst I tried to encourage these adolescents to tell their parents or tutors, this advice was not always acted upon for fear of being a 'grass'. This meant I had to try to empower them to deal with the bullies themselves. Sometimes the tactics were successful, but more often the victims would leave the college or change their courses. It was disgraceful that those who were bullied were put into the position of having to change courses, and at the same time to try and catch up on the work they had missed.

Signs of offline bullying

As a parent of an adolescent who appears to be bullied, look for signs of unusual behaviour. For example, he or she:

- May not wish to attend school or college.
- Regularly complains of feeling ill.
- Is not completing their homework on time.
- Shows signs of being anxious before or after school.
- Has trouble sleeping.
- Starts to use alcohol or drugs.
- Has physical injuries they cannot or will not explain.

It is now known that those adolescents who have been on the receiving end of being bullied may encounter low academic performance, self-harm, feelings of loneliness and changes in sleeping and eating patterns (Rothon et al., 2011). These issues could alter the course of a young person's life due to poor self-esteem and may result in long-term depression and anxiety.

Depression and Anxiety

Depression

The symptoms of depression range from feelings of unhappiness to feeling suicidal. These feelings are often accompanied by physical symptoms such as being constantly tired, having poor sleep, having no appetite, and generally the inability to be motivated to do anything. Sometimes being depressed may be the result of a relationship breakdown, or the loss of a loved one. In these situations, it is normal to feel depressed and, for most people, the depression will lift in time. However, when adolescents are constantly cyberbullied, they may become depressed without realising what is going on. I have counselled many young people experiencing depression but on first meeting them they usually say, "I'm a bit stressed out". Stress is different to anxiety and depression because stress is a reaction to being placed under pressure which makes it difficult to cope. It is important that you, as parents, recognise the difference between stress and depression, as being depressed usually carries a feeling of anxiety as well.

Anxiety

Anxiety is a feeling of worry or fear which may appear mild or be severe. It is a normal response to a threat, where the threat can be real or imagined. Anxious individuals sometimes display physical symptoms of sweating and a fast heartbeat. Extreme anxiety, when not treated, may lead to panic attacks where individuals experience shaking, a shortness of breath, nausea, dizziness, and a fear of losing control or going crazy.

As a counsellor, I have worked with many young people who were anxious for such a long time that their anxiety became part of their normal way of living. I believe it is necessary for adolescents to know what is causing their anxiety before adopting strategies to overcome it. Once they know the cause of their anxiety parents can help them to achieve a more positive view of themselves by using the following strategies.

- It is helpful for adolescents to write down what is causing their depression or anxiety.
- Let them know you value effort rather than perfection at anything they do.
- Encourage them to try new challenges, give praise for their successes.
- Help them set goals and make plans for things they would like to accomplish.
- Help them to discover and develop their talents, through clubs, groups, and activities.
- Encourage them to express themselves creatively, through art, drama, or music.
- Get them involved with voluntary projects that make a difference to someone else. This will help them to develop a more positive opinion of themselves.

Some of the above pursuits should help to build confidence, keep the problem in perspective and offer the chance to make new friends.

Finding the correct support

I suggest that young people who display 'severe' symptoms

of depression or anxiety or any other serious mental health issues caused by bullying, see a GP for onwards referral to a psychiatrist, psychologist, psychotherapist, or a counsellor. It can feel like walking through a minefield trying to sort out the best treatment for your adolescents, so here is a guide to the different types of help available:

Psychiatrists

Psychiatrists are medical doctors who diagnose illness and provide treatment and medication for complex mental health issues. They have a deep understanding of schizophrenia, depression, bipolar disorder, eating disorders and addiction. They can also provide emergency care for a sudden mental illness and help patients to manage a long-term mental health condition. Referrals are made by a GP to the NHS.

Psychologists

Clinical Psychologists who specialise in mental health issues should possess a Doctorate degree. They should also be accredited by The British Psychological Society (www.bps.org. uk) and may use one of the talking therapies which will be explained shortly. Referrals can be made to the NHS via a GP, or by self-referral to an independent psychologist.

Psychotherapists

Psychotherapists can choose from several approaches to help people to understand and explore how they feel. Some will also teach skills to help clients manage difficult emotions more effectively. Psychotherapists will need a degree in counselling psychology or a related subject. Referrals can be made by a GP, or by self-referral.

Counsellors

Counsellors help individuals with mental health difficulties, and while they do not need a degree, they should possess a formal qualification which is a two or three-year Diploma in Counselling. While areas of psychotherapy and counselling overlap, psychotherapists work on long-term concerns and have the training to reflect this. It might appear that counsellors are at the bottom of the pecking order, but many (including myself) continue with further training to obtain a Master or a Doctorate degree in counselling. Referrals can be made by a GP or self-referral.

—

Checking a professional's experience, training and qualifications is always advised, as this will give you a better understanding of how they can help support your adolescent's needs. For those parents who want to self-refer their adolescents, then I suggest you search the British Association for Counselling and Psychotherapy (www.bacp.co.uk) site and look for counsellors and psychotherapists who have been accredited by this organisation. The other alternative is to search for adolescent counselling services in your local area. When looking for a counsellor or psychotherapist you will come across different types of training which use diverse models. The main talking therapies are listed below.

Person-Centred

People who see a person-centred counsellor will be encouraged to bring their own issues for discussion, and the counselling is led by the client. Counsellors help individuals to explore their issues, feelings, beliefs, and behaviour, so they become more aware of their difficulties. They then help clients to realise what resources and support are available, so that they can work through their issues. Eventually clients discover their own abilities and gain sufficient confidence to cope with current and future problems.

Psychodynamic counselling or psychotherapy

This model attempts to help individuals understand long-standing conflicts from the past and become more self-aware and bring unconscious processes into consciousness. It also focuses on the fact that many personal issues in life are the result of mental processes that are hidden. Once individuals are aware of these conflicts, they can then choose what to do about them.

Cognitive Behavioural Therapy (CBT)

CBT is usually favoured by clinicians working for the NHS and is most common for treating anxiety and depression. It is based on the concept that people's thoughts, feelings, and actions are interconnected, and that negative thoughts and feelings can trap them in a vicious cycle. It aims to help individuals to deal with overwhelming problems in a more positive way by breaking them down into smaller segments. Individuals are shown how to change these negative patterns to improve the way they feel. CBT is a shorter method in that it deals with current problems, rather than focusing on past difficulties.

—

In extreme circumstances, a GP may recommend anti-depressants as a solution to treat depression while referring them to one of the recommended services. Please be aware that some anti-depressants prescribed to treat depression can increase the risk of suicide in the short-term amongst those who are already feeling suicidal. Anxiety treatment is based on a detailed assessment by qualified health practitioners. They will check if there are any biological causes for the anxiety and may include your adolescent keeping a diary of the situations when they feel anxious. Practitioners will also suggest different strategies to manage anxiety such as, removing oneself from the anxious environment and finding solutions to help the anxiety diminish over time.

Information for Parents

Practical advice

Keep a bullying diary and write down every incident after it happens in the format previously described and include the effect on your adolescent and whether he or she told anyone, and what any third parties said or did. Support adolescents by telling them they have done the right thing by reporting the bullying to you and encourage them to learn how to take charge of their safety by developing skills for preventing and stopping harassment themselves. For instance, walking away from the bully, avoiding those whose behaviour is problematic, and suggest that your adolescent takes a different route and walks with other pupils to and from school. Do not let the bullying dominate their lives.

Support from schools

If you believe your adolescent may be a victim of bullying, inform the school as soon as possible. Before approaching the school, list all the facts: what happened, who was involved, when it occurred, and who witnessed the incidents. By law, all schools must have procedures in place to prevent bullying, and parents should be informed of those procedures. I suggest you read online a document, *Preventing and tackling bullying: Advice for head teachers, staff and governing bodies* (www.gov.uk. Preventing Bullying, 2017). Although this report is primarily for teachers, there is also a lot of invaluable advice including how to stop bullying. Many schools offer different forms of support to help bullied adolescents, often mentors or counsellors. Allow the school time to deal with the problem, but stay in touch with them and arrange follow-up meetings to see how the situation is being resolved. I have seen many parents fail to stop their young people being bullied by resorting to telephone calls and not following these calls up in writing. In Appendix B there are template letters you can use to write to the class teacher, head of year, headteacher, and board of governors.

Helpful agencies

If you are not satisfied with the school's response you may wish to write to the LEA education department, or your local MP, or the Secretary of State. Template letters are also included in Appendix B, but this is a lengthy process. A word of caution, unless home-teaching, you can be prosecuted if you take your son or daughter out of school and do not provide them with an alternative method of teaching.

The police

If your young person is hurt, take photographs, see a doctor, and involve the police if they have been assaulted. You may wish to make a complaint to the police about intimidation, harassment, physical attacks, or threats. This is a wise thing to do if the bullies are over the age of criminal responsibility, which is ten years old in England and Wales. The police may be prepared to visit the bully's home to warn them off. However, it is unlikely that further action will follow unless there has been an assault seen by independent witnesses or a long campaign of harassment.

School sanctions for bullying

If your adolescent is the bully, schools have several options for dealing with bullying and you need to make your son or daughter aware of the sanctions. These include issuing a warning, contacting you as the parents, detention in internal exclusion within the school, fixed-term exclusion, and, as a last resort, permanent exclusion.

Information for Teachers

Teachers should follow the anti-bullying policy which is relevant to their school. The document *Preventing and tackling bullying: Advice for head teachers, staff and governing bodies* (www. gov.uk. Preventing Bullying, 2017) reminds schools how they can deal with bullying. School involvement in tackling bullying should not start at the point at which a pupil has been bullied – rather, a school should strive for excellence by developing an ethos to prevent bullying happening in the first place. When bullying does occur, it is important for schools to respond promptly, support the bullied pupil and ensure that the bullying does not happen again. There are things teachers can do to challenge bullying by encouraging adolescents to get help from the school counsellor and tell their parents what is happening.

Cyberbullying

Cyberbullying can also be defined with the measure of bullying described at the beginning of this chapter. But it takes on a new form when electronic devices are used and mainly consists of verbal aggression such as threatening to harass individuals, or relational aggression, that is, spreading rumours electronically. Cyberbullying is often carried out on social media platforms such as Facebook, Instagram, and Snapchat. It can also happen via email, chat rooms, Skype or through adolescents using their mobiles and text messaging.

In a report by *Status of Mind* (www.rsph.org.uk 2017) the authors claim that seven out of ten adolescents have experienced cyberbullying with 37 per cent of them saying they are bullied frequently. A study claimed that one third of adolescents who have been cyberbullied were targeted because of their size or weight (Cassidy et al., 2009). Most of the social networking sites have clear procedures for reporting online bullying. However, a national survey undertaken by Bullying UK (www.bullying.co.uk) identified that 91 per cent of young people who reported incidents of online bullying said that no action was taken.

Appearance-related cyberbullying

A study by Berne et al., (2014) investigated adolescents' experience of appearance-related (AR) cyberbullying. The researchers presented a hypothetical situation using two mock Facebook accounts. Two photos (one boy and one girl) were displayed on the new accounts and underneath each profile the researchers posted fictitious mean comments about the users' appearance. After viewing the Facebook profiles and reading the mean comments the adolescents were asked to respond to the following questions, "In what way are adolescents cyberbullied about their appearance?" and "What are the effects of cyberbullying?" (Berne et al., 2014).

The researchers found that all the adolescents agreed they used social media to post images of themselves looking their best, to receive as many 'likes' as possible. The participants explained that girls are cyberbullied, because of the need to attract attention to themselves. This presents a dilemma for the girls who said they are trying to live up to the media idealism by being skinny, having large breasts, a shapely bottom and perfect hair. At the same time the girls receive negative comments from their peers which disapprove of their height, breasts, and hair, but often the criticisms are about their weight. Added to which, in their effort to look good in their photos, the girls thought their sexual reputations could be damaged by being labelled a 'whore' or a 'slut' (Berne et al., 2014: 531).

The adolescents believed that cyberbullying is aimed at one's appearance because it seems to be a powerful tool to hurt the girls. One girl responded that if one of her peers seems insecure about her weight, she targets this aspect belonging to her peer, because she thinks it is an effective type of ammunition to use. One boy explained that if he tells the girls they are fat or ugly they will lose their confidence and feel bad about themselves (Berne et al., 2014). It appeared envy was another reason amongst some of the girls to cyberbully other girls. Another girl reported that one of her peer's had a life that was so "fucking perfect, she's got a perfect life, and I want that too", so she decided to write a nasty comment to change her peer's supposedly "perfect life" (Berne et al., 2014:529).

Some of the boys received cynical remarks about their appearance. For instance, interpretations by their peers of them having muscular bodies, when clearly, they do not. Photos of the boys seeming to look 'gay' provoked perceptions of negative comments, and some boys will try to avoid looking gay because these images do not fit in with their ideals of masculinity. This led to a few of them deciding not to post photos of themselves online.

There were differences reported between the boys and girls regarding the effects of being cyberbullied. Some boys said if they were cyberbullied for not displaying a muscular body, they would react violently, while others stated they would not be bothered (Berne et al., 2014). The girls explained they may become less confident, have reduced self-esteem, become depressed or even contemplate suicide (Berne et al., 2014). The results from this study show there is more potential for the girls to develop serious mental health issues through cyberbullying than boys.

Other forms of cyberbullying and harassment

Apart from the obvious forms of cyberbullying there are others which include harassment and are as follows:

- Spreading malicious rumours.
- Texting threatening or intimidating comments.
- Stalking online and continually harassing someone.

- Posting embarrassing or humiliating images without consent.
- Posting another person's details without their consent.
- Using someone's identity to set up a false profile (nationalbullyinghelpline.co.uk).

There are laws to protect someone who is on the receiving end of such unacceptable behaviour and they are explained in the section headed 'the police' shortly.

Information for Parents

Practical advice

If your son or daughter informs you that they have been cyberbullied, the first task is to discover how long the cyberbullying has been going on, the names of those involved and the forms of cyberbullying used. If there is evidence of the cyberbullying i.e. saved text messages, posts, comments, screenshots and so forth, have your adolescent show these to you so you can retain them for future evidence. Cyberbullying robs victims of their sense of control, but by including your adolescent in the process of resolving the issue, you help them to regain some of that control. Advise your son or daughter to ask the bully to stop sending distressing messages, change their passwords, contact details, and to keep personal information private. Blocking the bully will also help your adolescent regain power and reduce or eliminate one aspect of cyberbullying that makes it so damaging; that is the ability for the cyberbully to attack publicly at any hour of the day, and in any place.

Service provider

Familiarise yourself with the 'Terms of Use' for the service provider. Many websites prohibit harassment and if you report it through their established procedures, the content and/or the cyberbully should be removed from the site. If the individual responsible is unknown or refuses to take down the offensive material, contact the site directly to make a report and request that the content is taken down. The material posted may be in breach of the service provider's terms and conditions of use and can therefore be removed. Before you contact a web service provider, it is important to be clear about where the content is, for example by taking a screenshot of the material that includes the web address. If you ask the service provider to remove material that is not illegal, be clear to point out how it breaks the site's terms and conditions.

Support from schools

If your son or daughter is of school age, chances are high that the cyberbullying has spilled over into their school experience. I suggest you read *Preventing and tackling bullying: Advice for head teachers, staff and governing bodies* (www. gov.uk. Preventing Bullying, 2017) which has a section for parents with lots of helpful advice on working with the school to ensure that the cyberbullying is stopped and does not escalate.

The police

If the cyberbullying includes a realistic physical threat of harm, report it to the police immediately. Cyberbullying may also be a criminal offence, and many adolescents have been shocked to discover their actions constitute a crime and that they will have to bear the full consequences within the legal system. Chief Constable Andy Trotter who leads the ACPO Communication Group states that, "People who think they can remain anonymous when online and say and do things they wouldn't do in real life without any consequences or being found out; this is not the case. Reports of online credible threats that specifically target individuals and constitute harassment are taken very seriously and will be investigated by the police. Call your local police on 101 if you think someone is being threatened or harassed online" (nationalbullyinghelpline.co.uk).

If your adolescent is a cyberbully

Claire Lilley, technology expert for the NSPCC (www.nspcc. org.uk), one of the children's leading charities, believes that showing the consequences of receiving distressing comments about oneself and building empathy, is crucial to making sure adolescents do not become a cyberbully. In the parental guide in Chapter 5, I have outlined how parents can develop the skill of empathy. In the meantime, I suggest you help your son or daughter to reflect on how they would feel if they were in the position of being bullied themselves.

Information for Teachers

Creating a good school-parent relationship can help create an atmosphere of trust that encourages parents to raise concerns in an appropriate manner. Part of this is making sure that parents and carers are aware and understand how to communicate with the school. Schools should also make clear that it is not acceptable for pupils, parents, or colleagues to denigrate and bully school staff via social media in the same way that it is unacceptable to do so face to face.

—

Cyberbullying is more intrusive than offline bullying as adolescents can flee from a schoolyard bully by leaving, but that will not work in cyberspace. Texts, posts, and tweets reach victims at home, at school and in the community. Victims have fewer places to hide unless they disconnect from social media, which runs the risk of fuelling a sense of isolation. Cyberbullying does not set out to encourage the presence of a 'mob' mentality in which the responsibility for one's actions will be reduced. However, I believe online 'gang' behaviour can exist when cyberbullies revel in the attention they receive, their followers increase, and they perceive that they have become more popular. Trying to stop any form of bullying is an area that I feel is crucial for parents and teachers to try and prevent. As a counsellor I saw many young people who had been bullied who would then carry out self-harming behaviour or even try to commit suicide.

4

BODY IMAGE

Adolescence is a period of significant biological change which makes body image an important aspect of identity development. As well as feedback from their peers, the popular images of models distributed by the media affects what adolescents think about body image and how they perceive themselves (Huntermann & Morgan, 2001). If their ideal images are vastly different to their actual body shapes this can cause great unhappiness, resulting in a negative view of oneself, and lower self-esteem (Huntermann & Morgan, 2001).

Self-Esteem and Facebook

I will now describe a study undertaken by Gonzales and Hancock (2011) in which they identified that increased self-esteem could happen when students use Facebook under certain conditions. Facebook is designed to share information about oneself and by reflecting on such information, people can become aware of their own shortcomings, which subsequently lowers their self-esteem (Heine et al., 2008). However, some information represents positively biased aspects of oneself which may increase their self-esteem (Walther, 1996).

Gonzales & Hancock (2011) investigated whether a group of students who were asked to examine and update their profiles on Facebook would report higher levels of self-esteem, compared to another group who viewed other profiles in addition to their own. Both these groups were compared to a third group who reported measures of self-esteem by viewing their own images in a mirror.

The results demonstrate with the first group, exposure to information presented on one's Facebook profile enhances self-esteem, especially when a person edits information about the self, or selectively self-presents what they post (Gonzales & Hancock, 2011). These results are consistent with Walther's (1996) theory which claims that communication that is mediated by a computer (CMC) exceeds face-to-face interaction. Compared to face-to-face encounters, messages sent by CMC have a greater ability to develop and edit self-presentation, enabling an improved presentation of oneself to others. This means that the process of online self-presentation, where there is more time to create images, makes Facebook a unique source of self-awareness. The second group who looked at other's profiles reported lower levels of self-esteem than this group. And the third group reported that a non-edited view of the self (the mirror) is likely to decrease self-esteem (Gonzales & Hancock, 2011).

Changes to one's profile and paying attention to it (vs. other's profiles or looking in a mirror) has a positive effect on self-esteem, which suggests that selective self-presentation is a factor in shaping the resultant self-reports of self-esteem. The moral of this story is to tell your adolescents to edit their images to show their positive attributes, to only share with friends they know well, and not to distribute them haphazardly to audiences that they do not know. They may not get a high number of 'likes', but they may receive positive comments from those friends who care about them.

Gender and Body Image

Researchers Mikkola et al., (2008) noted that body image has become an essential part of adolescent identity. As part of their investigation into this topic they showed a group of adolescents a range of male and female silhouettes, with bodies ranging from very thin to very fat. The researchers asked participants to rate the silhouettes in relation to their current size, their ideal figure, the figure they expect the opposite sex to find attractive and the figure they think is the present cultural (media-based) body image. A body image scale was used to assess the adolescents' satisfaction of these categories.

Table 4.0 Satisfaction of Body Image (Mikkola et al., 2008:3083)

Gender	Current Size %	Ideal Figure for Self	Ideal Figure for Opposite Sex	Cultural (Media) Ideal Figure
Boys	68	Normal	Normal	Normal
Girls	45	Very thin (25%) *	Normal	Very thin (50%)
*Denotes % of girls who thought about their personal ideal figure vs. their cultural ideal figure				

Sixty-eight percent of the boys were satisfied with their current size, while, in contrast, 45 per cent of girls were satisfied with their current bodies. There was a difference of opinion concerning the cultural ideal where the boys favoured an average-sized figure, while half of the girls said their cultural figure was a very thin body. Results also show there is a further inconsistency between the girls' personal ideal and cultural ideal figures, with the girls reporting the latter category should be very thin. Such responses from the girls strengthen the argument they are influenced by images on social media. In a previous study, evidence was found that images on social media play an important part in how boys and girls feel about their body image, but the girls suffer more from body dissatisfaction than the boys (Palmgvist & Santavirta, 2006). That would seem to be the case with the results of this investigation.

Perceptions of Beauty

A study carried out by Chua and Chang (2016) investigated how adolescent girls show their self-presentation through posting selfies on Instagram, and how they characterise peer comparison taking place on this site (Chua & Chang, 2016).

Eighty-eight per cent of the girls reported that social media had a role in influencing them to achieve the standards of beauty that were portrayed. The girls copy the hair, make-up, and clothes worn by young famous celebrities, then create their own images and post them as selfies on their Instagram accounts. One girl described a trend where some of her peers cut their fringes so short, they looked stupid, but because this fashion was being promoted on social media her peers thought they looked lovely. The same girl explained she did not like her fringe being cut so short, but her peers got lots of 'likes' and so they must copy this trend to be considered beautiful

(Chua & Chang, 2016). A second girl described that when she was preparing a photo of herself, she wore her coolest clothes and portrayed a big smile to create the image she wanted to convey to her peers. In addition to copying each other there was detailed backstage planning of where their photos were taken. Another girl said that she would look for a place to take her photo which was worthy of being posted on her Instagram account (Chua & Chang, 2016). Some of the other girls analysed their peers' photographs, 'likes' and comments to learn the best way to create their own photos (Chua & Chang, 2016).

All the girls accumulated feedback from their friends by counting how many 'likes' and followers they received with the number of 'likes' taking precedence. Thirty-eight per cent of this group claimed that positive feedback about being pretty made them feel happy, while others became unhappy when their number of 'likes' decreased. One girl had over 300 followers, but when her Instagram account was deleted, she thought her life was over and cried for three days (Chua & Chang, 2016). Another girl reported the loss of four of her followers as humiliating as it made her feel lost and boring (Chua & Chang, 2016).

The above statements emphasise the need for these girls to receive lots of 'likes' or followers to feel valued by their peers. These examples show that peer comparison can have negative consequences, challenging girls' beliefs in their self-worth, reinforcing the peer norms shown on social media, which emphasise being pretty and thin, and generating disappointment with their appearance. Editing their self-images, such as back-stage preparations before their front-stage display, brings the girls closer to their ideal perception of beauty. But, being on Instagram becomes like entering a beauty competition, where girls accumulate 'likes' or followers to validate their success in winning peer recognition of their self–presentation (Chua & Chang, 2016).

The results from this study raise two important issues – insecurity, and low self-esteem, both of which are connected to peer comparison. Sixty-three per cent of the girls explained their insecurities were manifested by a fear of having 'ugly' or 'lame' pictures judged by their peers (Chua & Chang, 2016), as well as the desire to look as attractive as their friends. One girl commented that when she looks at her peers' selfies, she feels ugly and wants to get a pair of scissors and cut her hand. As well as self-harming, 22 per cent of the girls said they or their friends practised self-induced vomiting because they felt they were not as attractive as their peers. Another girl described how her best friend got a stomach ulcer when she stopped eating. This girl tried to help her friend, but her friend starved herself, and when she did eat, she would go to the toilet and vomit (Chua & Chang, 2016). Low self-esteem was noted by another girl who explained she wanted to be attractive, as people generally say she is ugly. As a result, she posts lots of pictures to let her peers see that she is in fact pretty (Chua & Chang, 2016).

I am struck by the amount of effort which these girls put in to achieve a self-presentation that is Instagram-worthy in the hope that their peers will view them as beautiful. For many in this group, insecurity and poor self-esteem result in a self-perpetuating cycle of extreme distress caused by the impact of peer influence as peers' judgements are made public. Well over half of the girls reported they felt insecure about having their photos judged negatively by their peers, with a quarter saying they resort to vomiting to manage such feelings.

Anorexia and Bulimia

As seen in Chua and Chang's (2016) study, some of the participants resorted to eating disorders or self-harming behaviour to manage their low self-esteem. Issues concerning eating disorders are now discussed, whilst manging self-harm is featured in Chapter 9.

Although social media itself is not the sole cause of an eating disorder, it can play a role in influencing people to engage in disordered patterns of eating. Some adolescents begin to constantly compare themselves to thin models, their peers, as well as famous social media users, and they begin to feel inadequate. With the increased use of social media, it has been increasingly difficult to avoid the constant peer pressure surrounding the ideal body type. Social media's presence in everyday life is so large that individuals now care about the opinions of people they have never met. Social media trolls use these sites to talk negatively about individuals' images and this affects the emotional well-being of people who are already struggling with their relationship with food.

A preoccupation with one's body image can result in eating disorders such as anorexia and bulimia. Individuals may be more likely to get an eating disorder if they have been criticised for their eating habits, body shape or weight, are extremely anxious about being thin, if they feel pressure from their peers, have been sexually abused, or have a family member with a history of eating disorders, depression, or alcohol or drug addiction (Ritchie, 2000). Men and women of any age can become anorexic or bulimic, but it is most common in young women and typically starts in the mid-teens. Victoria Allen, a science correspondent for the *Daily Mail*, reported that admissions to hospitals for eating disorders for young people under eighteen have more than doubled in the past decade. They have increased from 1742 for the year 2010–2011 to 4540 in 2018–2019 (www.dailymail.co.uk).

Anorexia

Anorexia is a serious mental health condition which concerns a loss of appetite along with an attempt to gain control over unmanageable feelings. Individuals control their appetite by creating a system of eating little and surviving on less, where eventually they may starve themselves to death. They may have anxiety, particularly about eating in front of other people, show poor self-esteem along with a low confidence of self, have difficulty remembering and poor concentration. Starvation affects all the body's organs, including the brain and muscle tissue. There are many physical problems associated with anorexia such as: gut, heart, bowel and kidney complaints, feeling tired and cold because of poor circulation, an increased risk of infertility, osteoporosis, and erosion of tooth enamel. Anorexics also have a weakened immune system and become anaemic. Possible signs of someone who is anorexic include:

- Doing lots of exercise.
- If under eighteen, weight and height is lower than expected.
- Missing meals or avoiding eating any foods they see as fattening.
- Believing they are fat when they show a healthy weight.
- Taking appetite suppressants to reduce hunger.

- Periods stopping (pre-menopausal) or not starting in young females.
- Feeling dizzy or lightheaded.
- Dry skin and hair loss.
- Inducing vomiting or taking laxatives.
- Lack of sexual interest.
- Swelling of hands, face, and feet.

If people do not eat enough, their bodies go into survival mode and they develop a soft downy hair called 'lanugo'. With anorexics, eating is associated with expressing a desire to become dependent, but at the same time allowing themselves to be dependent is terrifying. The paradox is, that while they want to believe they do not need to become dependent on others, they may end up in hospital with twenty-four-hour care, where others must feed them (Ritchie, 2000). Anorexia remains one of the leading causes of death related to mental health problems, with deaths due to physical complications or suicide.

Bulimia

People who have bulimia go through a ritual where they eat lots of food in a short amount of time, this is called 'bingeing' and subsequently make themselves vomit after. Some individuals also use laxatives because they think they can empty the food out before it is absorbed into their bodies. Thus, they believe this will help them to lose weight. They will also carry out excessive exercise to try to prevent gaining weight. This is known as 'purging'. Bulimia is often a vicious cycle of bingeing and purging when life becomes too stressful to cope. These destructive feelings can be removed by the action of eating. Once the food is inside their stomachs it turns 'bad' and negative feelings such as shame come to the fore (Ritchie, 2000). The individual then feels they have got to get rid of these bad feelings down the toilet by vomiting. Once this is done, bulimics feel relieved, and able to face the world again until the next purging episode.

Bulimia is a serious mental health problem with many physical issues such as tiredness and weakness caused by not getting the right nutrients, tooth enamel damage from persistent vomiting, damage to the vocal chords and throat, absent or irregular periods, swollen glands, fits and muscle spasms, kidney damage, permanent constipation, osteoporosis, and a risk of cardiac arrest due to a decrease in potassium which creates an electrolyte imbalance. Other signs of bulimia are:

- Exercising a lot more than usual.
- Going to the toilet after meals.
- Isolating from others.
- Dry skin and brittle fingernails.
- Scars on fingers, knuckles, or backs of hands.
- Bad breath.
- Constant eating which becomes uncontrollable once the eating has started.
- Lack of sexual interest.

Psychologically one can understand bulimia as being in touch with an individual's feelings and the need for relationships with significant others. However, these feelings are experienced to the degree that they are overwhelming and feel destructive, which means the bulimia is used to control these intense emotions.

Guides for Parents and Teachers

Parents

Encourage your son or daughter to engage in activities and do something enjoyable with friends. Try and persuade them to have mindful eating behaviours such as focusing on the food that they like and cooking healthy meals. Make sure they are surrounded by loved ones during mealtimes. Encourage them to practise relaxation techniques to develop a natural response when stress levels are increased.

Getting professional support as soon as possible gives adolescents the best chance of recovering from anorexia or bulimia. When I was working with young people who had an eating disorder, I immediately referred them to specialist services through their GP. I did this because the diagnosis of eating disorders is so complex, consisting of psychological, biological, and environmental factors. Once referred, their GP will ask questions about the young person's eating habits, how they are feeling, and will check their overall health and weight. They may also refer them for some blood tests to make sure their weight loss is not caused by something else. If a GP believes a young person is anorexic or bulimic, they will refer them to an eating disorder specialist. These are highly trained professionals who are equipped to help individuals establish self-soothing techniques, meal plans, and personalised coping mechanisms. In time, individuals can build the resilience needed to fully recover from their eating disorder.

Young people might be frightened to get professional help as they may worry that the treatment will make them overweight. But readers need to be rational and assist them in seeking help. Parents can talk in confidence to an adviser from Beat, the UK's leading charity supporting those affected by eating disorders (www.beateatingdisorders.org.uk). You can reach them in person by calling their adult helpline on 0808 801 0677 or youth helpline on 0808 801 0711. However, be aware of the role social media plays, as there are several dangerous pro-anorexia and pro-bulimia websites that encourage eating disorders, which you and the adolescents you care for need to avoid.

Teachers

To help adolescents deal with their underlying issues of self-esteem relating to eating disorders, educational programmes might be the best approach to provide guidance and support for users of social media. Teachers can play an important role in tackling issues that arise from peer comparison and excessive attachment to the number of 'likes', as well as encouraging young people to adopt a critical view of the limited range of body shapes presented on social media. Teachers could also make adolescents aware, particularly girls, that false personas exist in the virtual world, and to understand that information on social media should not define their identity and self-worth.

5

RACIAL DISCRIMINATION

The terms 'race' and 'ethnicity' are often used simultaneously; however, they have different meanings. The term 'race' is linked to humans who share the same physical characteristics, such as skin colour and facial features, whereas ethnicity is connected to common religious, linguistic, or cultural origins. Racial discrimination which exists in the offline world can be perceived as the demeaning or oppression of people from black, Asian, and other minority ethnic backgrounds (BAME). Racism consists of verbal and physical abuse, racist jokes, ridicule of cultural differences (food, dress, language), possession and distribution of racist material, racist graffiti, and incitement of others to behave in a racist way.

A Brief History of Racial Discrimination in the UK

Racism in the UK has long been associated with rising immigration after WWII. The increase in immigration was due partly to a shortage in the workforce after the war which led to many migrants arriving in the UK in search of a better life. Immigration peaked in the 1960s, and during the latter part of the 1970s the UK became defined by a new group of multicultural citizens. With this cultural change, racism began to escalate.

Racism in British football

British football is useful as an example of how racism escalated as, prior to the 1970s, football was traditionally a white player's sport. An increase in young, high-profile black players saw an increase in football-related racism, racist abuse, and chanting became frequent occurrences inside football grounds (Kassimeris, 2009). Some black players felt their position was untenable and left the game (Back et al., 2001), while other players were reluctant to report incidents for fear of an acceleration of abuse. This resulted in the scale of football racism staying hidden for many years.

Individual racism declined in British football from the 1990s through legislation that led to the Football Offences Act (1991) which made racist chanting unlawful. However, in some of the clubs and associated governing bodies of the sport, racism remains a fundamental problem (House of Commons 2012). Because of the failure to recognise racism as a societal and institutional issue, anti-racism groups have formed, arising from the desire of individuals to make a difference rather than from a political or institutional influence (Bonnet, 2000).

Show Racism the Red Card (www.theredcard.org) is one example of an anti-racist group. It is the largest educational charity in the UK and aims to combat racist views. It consists of education workers, sessional workers and ex-professional footballers who promote their anti-racism views by providing education and workshops to young people and adults focussing on the causes and the consequences of racism. The educational packs and workshops that this charity provide are supported by celebrity football players who add their personal experiences of a form of prejudice that is often hidden. The workshops are interactive, designed to develop empathy, and to encourage discussion and critical thinking. The role of empathy is important when addressing conversations on differences such as age, race, gender, and sexual orientation. Under the section for parents and teachers I have included information on how you may develop this skill and pass it onto the adolescents in your care.

Adolescent Development of Racial Identity

By the age of ten, most children can recognise both obvious and covert discriminatory actions towards them (McKown & Weinstein, 2003), but it is during early adolescence (10–14 years) that they begin to understand the implications of race for one's daily life (Umaña-Taylor, 2016). In the same context, during late adolescence (15–19 years) they have a clearer grasp of abstract notions of racism (such as civil rights which include protection by law from discrimination) and the significance of these for their experiences in society (Quintana & McKown, 2008). Racial inequalities in health and well-being are thought to first occur in adolescence with a chain reaction that may last across their entire life span (Sanders-Phillips et al., 2009). Therefore, this is a crucial time to investigate the impact of racial discrimination because of the growing cognitive (the way in which the brain/mind makes sense of incoming information) and identity developmental processes that adolescents experience during this phase. These two processes are the foundations for perceiving racial discrimination and its ongoing consequences (Brown & Bigler, 2005), particularly from a mental health point of view.

Early and late adolescents have different vulnerabilities to racism. It may be that as their cognitive development unfolds, early adolescents are especially vulnerable to the long-term effects of social criticism. This is because they are only gradually acquiring the more sophisticated cognitions (formal operational thinking in which they learn how to think logically and make sense of abstract concepts such as thinking creatively and solving problems), to help them manage their experiences of racial discrimination (Brittian et al., 2013). Compared to older adolescents, they have more well-formed notions of their own ethnic identity and how others may view their racial group (Umaña-Taylor et al., 2014). But older adolescents are more likely to encounter racial discrimination at school where negative perceptions of peers which influence this type of behaviour may occur (Benner & Graham, 2011).

Racism in UK Secondary Schools

It seems sensible that teachers should have knowledge of and receive training on how to prevent or minimise racial discrimination in their schools. Sadly, that does not appear to be the case. Previous studies into the achievement of BAME pupils has shown that teachers' roles are essential in shaping the experiences and outcomes of such pupils (Maylor et al., 2006; Maylor et al., 2009) regardless of their class background (Gillborn et al., 2012).

Dr Remi Joseph-Salsibury and colleagues (2020) explored the nature of racism that existed in secondary schools by analysing data from interviews with teachers who worked in schools across Greater Manchester. The researchers identified several areas of the education system that need to change to tackle racial discrimination that is happening to BAME pupils. Whilst I provide a summary of their points that are relevant to this chapter, I would urge all teachers to look at their report which is available online, and further details are included in the guide for teachers at the end of this chapter.

Nearly all the teachers claimed there was lack of racial diversity within the current teaching profession; schools employ mainly white teachers, and in some schools, teachers are exclusively white. The teachers highlighted the role of 'racial literacy' which refers to the capacity to understand the ways in which race and racism work in society. It also involves having the language, skills, and confidence to utilise that knowledge in teaching practice (Guinier, 2004). As there is currently no training in this area, it is left up to the teachers' understanding of racism to use their own judgement. Several raised concerns about their own racial literacy, and many more discussed their worries with their colleagues. I believe the teaching profession should view racial literacy the same way they view literacy of reading, writing and numeracy. Without racial literacy being taught to young people, they too are at a disadvantage in how they engage with people from different cultural backgrounds. This was evident in one account from a male BAME teacher. He expressed concern that the current history curriculum is too narrow, consisting as it does of kings and queens, with no mention of important facts such as colonialism, the East India Company, and slavery (Joseph-Salsibury et al., 2020).

While many of the teachers said that their schools had policies for dealing with racism, some of them claimed that their policies were unclear, or they did not know of a policy. School policies can offer guidance to teachers to ensure that responses are consistent and can help pupils to refer to these policies to understand the disapproval of racism. The researchers conclude with a recommendation that anti-racism should be located at the heart of our education system. It should be echoed in school policies, the curriculum, the racial demographic of the teaching profession, and in the expertise and knowledge of the teachers (Joseph-Salsibury et al., 2020).

Another report carried out by the YMCA (www.ymca.org. uk) among groups of BAME young people reported that 95 per cent of participants claimed they had witnessed racist language when at school, and 49 per cent said they believed racism was the biggest barrier to academic attainment. Most of this group felt that they had to change to be acknowledged in society. For example, there have been strict school policies concerning hairstyles which have resulted in some black children being excluded. Others explained they had to change the texture of their hair and the way it grows to be accepted in schools and claimed that teachers suggest black afro-textured hair is untidy and needs brushing. Participants felt they had been labelled as unintelligent and aggressive at school, which led to higher rates of exclusion, and also felt it was difficult to speak about racist issues at school because racist language is often used.

Racism in the Workplace and Communities

The YMCA report claimed just over three quarters of the participants reported they heard and witnessed racist language in the workplace. When taking the next steps into employment, young black people feel that employer prejudice affects their chances of getting a job, with 54 per cent viewing bias at the recruitment stage as the main barrier to employment. When asked about police attitudes to race, the majority of young BAME people said they do not trust the police to act fairly towards them. More than half of young black people were worried about being falsely accused of a crime.

Denise Hatton, chief executive of YMCA England and Wales, sums up eloquently the way that society needs to change to ensure that young people from BAME populations receive the same opportunities as white adolescents. She says, "It is shameful that young black people growing up in the UK continue to do so within a society that engulfs them with racist language and discriminatory attitudes. Bias and barriers chip away at and ultimately shape the life experiences of young black people in the UK, putting them at a significant disadvantage. To improve the lives and experiences of young black people in a meaningful way, systems embedded within institutions must be reviewed and changed. However, we cannot do this without building a bridge to a community which has been beaten into fundamentally not trusting the very systems that need their help to be changed. Change must come swiftly, collaboratively, meaningfully and with longevity" (www.ymca.org.uk).

Potential Health Risks

Offline racial discrimination

In a review Benner, et al., (2018) examined studies with adolescents aged ten to 20 years of age to ascertain whether their perceptions of offline racial discrimination were linked to their socioemotional distress (depression, self-esteem, and positive well-being), academic success, and risky health behaviours.

The researchers' results identified that racial discrimination was nearly always connected to depression, low self-esteem, and poorer well-being, with the strongest link connected to depressive symptoms (Benner et al., 2018). The researchers found more evidence of racial discrimination in early adolescence which overlaps with the transition to high school. This is a time when pupils often struggle with the new educational environment and a more challenging academic curriculum (Benner et al., 2018). Managing this transition may disrupt an adolescent's ability to manage racial discrimination, thus resulting in greater challenges to academic adjustment at this stage of their lives. There is evidence that discrimination by teachers increases from early to mid-adolescence (Hughes et al., 2007), which may also contribute to the heightened effects of discrimination during this time. Adolescents' risky health behaviours linked to racial discrimination were delinquency, anger issues, alcohol and substance misuse and unprotected sex.

Online racial discrimination

I refer to the definition of online racial discrimination described by Tynes et al., (2016) in which they say, online racism is the belittling of, or excluding, people or groups because of their race or ethnicity, by using symbols, voice, video, images, text, and graphic representations. Online forms of racial discrimination occur in social networking sites, chat rooms, discussion boards, through text messaging, web pages, online videos, music, and online games.

Research carried out by Tynes et.al., (2016) explored whether the amount of time pupils spend online is associated with individual online racism that directly targets an individual because of his or her race or ethnicity. They examined the impact of receiving such comments by asking adolescents about their externalising behaviour (comprising of antisocial acts e.g. aggression and problem behaviour), acts that are considered victimless (e.g. substance misuse), as well as measuring for depressive symptoms and anxiety (Tynes et.al, 2016).

The results showed that, on average, adolescents spent between two to four hours online per day and that extended time online was associated with increased online racial discrimination. The results also demonstrated that the amount of time spent online is related to poor mental health outcomes with associations between race-related victimisation and depressive symptoms, anxiety, and externalising behaviour. The biggest link was an increase in anxiety (Tynes et al., 2016). This presents a problem for adolescents who wish to go online to study, make new friends and so forth. Instead of reaping the rewards that social media can bring for some BAME adolescents, this can hinder their academic outcome and thus lower their confidence and self-esteem.

Guides for Parents and Teachers

Parents

Parents should read their adolescent's school's anti-racism policy and follow their guidelines on how to report racist discrimination if their son or daughter is being discriminated against. An anti-bullying policy may advise that all incidents with racist connotations should be reported to the headteacher or the person who is responsible for safeguarding. In each situation a written record will be kept, and the incident should be reported to the Board of Governors. If necessary, use the templates I have previously described to eradicate bullying (Appendix B). I would also recommend utilising the strategies I have outlined to increase your son or daughter's self-esteem that are shown in the bullying chapter if you feel they are not coping.

How empathy is helpful

If you are willing to learn how to develop empathic skills this will stand you in good stead when dealing with the immediate effect of racial discrimination that your son or daughter may be experiencing. You do not need formal training to develop empathy, and you don't need to understand everything about someone to make them feel respected and valued. Displaying empathy is a learned behaviour consisting of an ability to recognise and understand another person's thoughts and feelings with some degree of accuracy.

Join a project

Consider the last time you thought about race, and racial discrimination. Ask yourself how frequently you are in social environments where most people are of a different cultural background to you, and how comfortable or uncomfortable you feel when faced with such settings. Working on a project with other people reinforces everyone's individual expertise and minimises the differences that can divide people.

I deliberately chose to take up employment with Sheffield MIND as a counsellor to establish a new counselling service where I would carry out assessments with BAME clients. I wanted to do this as Sheffield has a more diverse cultural population than York where I was living, and I needed to gain experience of working with different cultures.

Examine your biases

I encourage readers to consider any biases you have towards the BAME communities. Being biased is having a preconceived opinion about something or someone – and we all have biases, sometimes they are unconscious – that interfere with our ability to listen and empathise. Whilst working for Sheffield MIND I sat alongside a young Kurdish male immigrant who had entered the UK illegally after having escaped from his war-torn country. I initially felt out of my depth because of my lack of knowledge about his cultural background, and not understanding the terror he must have endured. Normally under these conditions my training would have helped me out by saying to a new client, "I'm not sure what help you need from me" and then wait to see what the response was. Clients would usually give me a list of the issues that are pressing, and we would together prioritise the list. I could not do that, as by using an interpreter I felt that any questions I asked him could be misinterpreted and make things confusing. Foolishly, my unconscious bias of wanting to use a western view of carrying out assessments did not work with this client. I realised in the first five minutes I would need to adopt a different approach to help him, and this is described shortly.

Practise active listening

Being empathic involves listening on an emotional as well as at a thinking level, and this process can be associated with listening with a 'third ear'. This is because, just as one can tune into a piece of music and feel the emotions that are underneath the lyrics of the song, the same process happens when one is empathic. One of the most valuable tools I recommend linked to empathy is to concentrate on the here-and-now of the experience that is going on between you and the person you are engaging with.

To use the young man I have described as an example, instead of going through the prescribed assessment list of questions, I used my empathic skills to tell me (through the interpreter) how he ended up in the UK. This gave him an opportunity to tell me about the horrors he had witnessed. I picked up on his distress by noticing his body language and tone of voice. By listening to his interpreter, I was able to tell that he had fled from his village, been tortured, and suffered inhumane treatment from the security guards in his country. By using empathy, I ascertained what he needed and was able to refer him to another suitable agency for ongoing counselling and to take care of his welfare needs.

You can practise active listening with your family, friends, and colleagues. Go beyond the small talk; ask them how they are and what is going on in their daily lives. Put away your mobiles when you are having conversations, even with the people you see every day, so you can fully listen to what they are saying and appreciate their situation. Notice their facial expressions, gestures, and body language, all of which can convey more emotions than their words. Look for signs that they are experiencing an emotion. There are six primary emotions that are common to all cultures which are happiness, sadness (depression), fear (anxiety/stress), disgust, anger, and surprise (a nice surprise or a nasty shock) (Gross, 2004).

Learn to use your body language to show that you are open to listening; uncross your arms, lean slightly forwards if sitting down, and make eye contact.

Try not to interrupt them when they are speaking and practise 'paraphrasing' (rephrasing a sentence) which is an empathic skill to facilitate a discussion, for example:

Adolescent: "All my friends have read horrible things that people say about me on Facebook and I don't think I can go back to class."

Try not to paraphrase like a parrot – e.g.

Parent: "Your friends have read horrible things about you and you can't go back there."

Instead use responses like:

Parent: "It seems you might be frightened to go back into your class. What's the worst thing that can happen to you if you decide to go back in?"

The first sentence is to acknowledge feelings, while the second sentence opens the discussion up further. Responding to these types of statements using open-ended questions such as how come, when and what, will require more thought than a simple yes or no answer. The offline world provides many opportunities for enhancing empathy, and readers need to look for them and practise.

Step into your adolescent's shoes

If your adolescent's behaviour is different and he or she seems upset, acknowledge that he or she might feel stressed, but then go further. Consider what it is like to live in his or her daily life. How much homework do they have? How much sleep do they get? When did their behaviour change? If you are unsure of your son or daughter's feelings, just ask them.

Teaching empathic skills to adolescents

Even if your sons or daughters do not initiate conversations about issues of racism you need to find ways to bring up this topic. Ask about the groups they identify with at school and what are the stereotypes that are associated with such groups. It is natural for adolescents to stick with the groups they feel most comfortable with, but I would encourage you to provide other opportunities where your adolescents can interact with peers from different cultural backgrounds.

If adolescents learn to be empathic, they may be less likely to inflict racial discrimination on others by virtue of the fact they will become kinder to each other. Developing empathy in adolescents is important as it teaches them to reflect, observe and think about their own behaviour. It also helps them to notice and name feelings in real-life situations such as characters on television (breakfast programmes or the news). There are examples on television where someone has been racially discriminated against. One way to get someone to empathise with others is to ask them what they think these people are feeling (from the list of universal emotions) based on their non-verbal communication, facial expressions, body language, and tone of voice. Studies show that when young people develop empathy, as well as not voicing racist views, they also display higher academic achievement, develop better communication skills, are less likely to bully others, have fewer emotional disorders, and will engage in more positive relationships (Allemend et al., 2015).

Teachers

Teachers should follow their school's anti-racism policy. Policies should detail how schools intend to combat racism, as well as offering guidance on responses to interpersonal racist incidents. A school's governing body should make sure that all staff understand and implement this policy, all staff training on anti-racism is carried out, the policy is made available to visitors, contractors, service providers and others associated with the school, and the governors are made aware of racist incidents.

Teachers will benefit from reading *Race and Racism in English Secondary Schools,* a report by Joseph-Salsibury (2020), as it gives clear guidance as to how schools may tackle racism. The Show Racism the Red Card website has an excellent online guide for teachers who would like to know more about promoting anti-racism in their schools. Click on the link which says Our Story, then scroll down the text to Education Packs; the book is called *Guidance for Initial Teacher Trainers Preparing student teachers to tackle racism and promote equality in the classroom.* In this publication, examples are provided for teachers explaining how to get their pupils to understand what racism consists of and the damage it causes. Also, I recommend you read *Young, discriminated, and Black: the true colour of institutional racism in the UK* (www.ymca.org.uk) which provides a broader view of racism including many poignant comments made by the young people who participated in this report. I encourage teachers to learn how to use empathy as part of their ongoing professional development.

—

Finally, I wish to acknowledge the work of Black Lives Matter, a global civil rights group which regularly campaigns against institutional racism and violence towards black people and speaks out against police brutality and racial inequality. Sadly, the evidence I have presented in this chapter confirms that racism does exist in the UK. However, many of the young people I have spoken to may be quicker to challenge intolerance of racist comments than adolescents of past generations. Parents and teachers should use this new intolerance to promote critical discussions and iron out the topic of difference, with a view to communicating positive values to all our young people. Although I realise that racial discrimination extends far beyond families and schools, I believe if parents and teachers work together to combat racism then this would be a start in giving BAME adolescents the opportunities that are available to their white counterparts, and at the same time improving their academic chances and well-being. It may also help future generations to embrace people from diverse cultures to their own, and not to feel threatened by the issue of difference.

6

SEXUAL ORIENTATION IDENTITY
DEVELOPMENT

During adolescence, young people explore and become interested in the development of their sexual orientation. This includes the emotional, romantic, or sexual attraction that an individual feels towards another person (Rosario & Schrimshaw, 2014). This definition is different to sexual identity which is explained in the next chapter. Young people generally explore their sexual orientation in several environments, for example, with their families, and through peer networks. Although individuals in these environments provide support for those identifying as heterosexual, adolescents who identify as lesbian, gay, bisexual, or transgender (LGBT), may find they do not receive the support they need from these groups. That is because LGBT adolescents may not feel comfortable telling their families or peers because they may face discrimination. This chapter highlights how adolescents are turning to online facilities to explore their sexual identity orientation and some of the consequences of that decision.

I draw a distinction between homosexual behaviour (having sex with someone of the same sex) and homosexual identity (seeing oneself as part of the LGBT group). I am choosing this distinction because some people may have sex with someone of the same sex, but their sexual orientation identity may change later, i.e. they may be experimenting, or alternatively may not have 'come out' (this phrase refers to openly declaring one's sexual orientation).

Different Sexual Orientations and Gender

Male homosexuality

Homosexuality in men can cause social problems and has been studied at great length by many psychiatrists. Readers may be familiar with many of the alleged 'causes' regarding this activity. Much of the research on this subject falls into two categories. The 'nature' view claims that gay men are born with an extra gene, or too many or too few sex hormones such as oestrogen. Alternatively, the 'nurture' camp takes the view that it is one's choice – potentially through absent fathers, a fear of negative sexual experience with someone of the other sex or having over-demanding mothers. Behind much of the research on gay men there is a perception that if a search for the cause can be identified, then a 'cure' can be found. The belief that there is something abnormal about gay orientation that needs correcting or treating is still held by some people today, because they believe gay people are suffering from psychological disorders (West, 2017).

Female homosexuality

Research into gay women is less prevalent than that into gay men because, as West (2017) claimed, lesbians are less vocal than gay men, fewer articles have been written about them, and they have not been legislated against. Prior to the late 1970s, psychological theory and research on lesbians was rare. The research that existed focused primarily on lesbianism as attributable to genetic predisposition (Bene, 1965) or early socialisation, particularly those aspects concerning the importance of negative childhood experiences with their fathers (Loney, 1973). Since then, the removal of homosexuality from the Diagnostic and Statistical Manual of Mental Disorders (DSM) and the increase in feminist views, has meant there has been a change in the emphasis of psychological theory towards the normalisation of lesbianism (Ellis, 2015).

—

Some studies into sexual orientation provoke controversy for a variety of reasons, including that they might cause harm to lesbians and gay men (Ellis, 2015). Many homosexual people have been forced to undergo 'treatments' to change their sexual orientation. Men were subjected to electric shock treatment, brain surgery, castration, hormone injections and long-term therapy in a bid to try and change their sexual orientation. Many lesbians were subjected to psychiatric 'treatment' with the goal of curing them of their lesbianism. All these treatments have proved fruitless. The motivation for searching for an 'origin' of homosexuality reveals homophobia, and for homosexual people who live in countries with no law to protect them, these dangers are particularly serious (Ellis, 2015). I must explain my position at the outset. I do not think it matters what influences someone to be attracted to their own gender, or to both, and the primary aim of relationships is to be oneself and lead a fulfilling life.

Bisexual individuals

Bisexual individuals have the potential to be attracted, romantically and/or sexually, to people of more than one gender. This attraction may not be at the same time, not in the same way, and not to the same degree.

Transgender

Transgender is a term used to describe people whose gender identity, gender expression or behaviour does not conform to that typically associated with the sex to which they were assigned at birth. For example, a person identifies as a female but has a male body. Some people have treatment to accept and confirm their identity, while others may embark on significant changes like changing their voice and having hormone treatment and surgery. Accurate diagnosis of transsexualism depends upon a licenced psychotherapist completing a thorough assessment, including case history, psychological tests, and a comprehensive series of therapy sessions (Ramsey, 1996).

Online Sexual Orientation Identity Development

Before social media was introduced, the way that members of the LGBT groups met like-minded people was usually when they reached the age of 18 and were able to frequent gay bars and clubs. Today, some adolescents who use social media platforms will want to share intimate aspects of their lives. By using these sites, the question arises of how social exclusion from families and peer groups may be experienced differently online, especially for those in the LGBT group who may be growing up in homophobic cultures.

Internet facilitation of the sexual orientation development of gay/bisexual young males

A study by Harper et al., (2016) explored the positive sexual health benefits for gay and bisexual young men who used the following facilities on the internet: chat rooms, message boards, forums, email, Instant messaging (IM), and blogs. Readers, please note these are not the typical networking sites such as Facebook, Instagram, Twitter etc, which are normally used by this age group to link with others with a view to maintaining and increasing their friendships.

Many of the participants reported learning about the realities of living as gay or bisexual young men through reading the life stories of other gay or bisexual individuals posted on the above facilities. For some of them, seeing explicit images of gay and bisexual men was arousing which led them to realise they were in fact attracted to other young men, thus enabling them to come to terms with their sexual orientation (Harper et al., 2016).

These sites offer gay and bisexual young men the opportunities to explore their sexual orientation in environments where they can control when, how, and how much disclosure about their orientation they wish to provide to others (Pingel et al., 2013). Several participants discussed how they came out to their friends online. The perception was this was an easier way to tell those friends with whom they had been connected for a longer period or who they considered to be their best friend. This was because the participants felt their friends would require a more detailed explanation (Harper et al., 2016).

For most of this group the sites served to communicate with other gay and bisexual young men. These connections were first established through a variety of gay and bisexual websites and continued communication occurred through email, IM, and chat rooms. One young man explained that the internet was useful to connect with others as it was impossible to access a gay or bisexual community in his town. Some participants reported that they entered chat rooms or posted messages on forums and message boards specifically with the purpose of obtaining a sexual partner. Most of these events involved one-time sexual encounters, but others did report having multiple contacts over time with a sexual partner they met through these sites.

The platforms also provide this group the opportunity to go beyond virtual connections, by facilitating face-to-face connections with other gay and bisexual men (Harper et al., 2016). By connecting with other young men on gay and bisexual websites, participants had the security of knowing that they were communicating with other individuals who shared their attraction to males, so they did not have to worry about making incorrect assumptions about sexual orientation during face-to-face interactions (Harper et al., 2016). This was a situation that many feared would result in physical and emotional harm if the receptive individual harboured homophobic and heterosexist views. However, the anonymity of these sites made many of the participants feel safe enough to come out to strangers. One young man described how he would ask questions through forums about how to protect himself from potential harm. If he felt safe enough, he would then meet the individual face to face (Harper et al., 2016).

To summarise this study, accessing these sites enabled this group to explore their sexual orientation and to realise they were gay or bisexual. These young men connected online to others where they shared their thoughts, and eventually they came out to family and friends. Some of them arranged offline meetings which were for friendship, while others were for sexual encounters. This group of participants described that the facilities previously described played a positive role in helping them to embrace their sexual orientation.

Analysis of bisexual and lesbian Facebook accounts

An investigation was carried out by Rubin and McCelland (2015) into young adolescent girls who identified as being bisexual or lesbian. One of the purposes of this study was to identify how this group managed the psychological process in navigating the practice of expressing their sexual orientation on Facebook.

All the adolescents described the dread of being judged by their family or friends because of the stigma that is attached to being perceived as a lesbian, or bisexual, in their communities or their schools. Most of the participants came from families where it was traditional for a man to marry a woman. One girl reported she had to dress up in clothes like her mum and sister in which she felt uncomfortable (Rubin & McCelland, 2015). Others had derogatory online comments from family members. One comment was that a girl's younger brother said that girls who are lesbians or bisexuals should be called 'sluts', while another girl's father described all lesbians as women who look like men (Rubin & McCelland, 2015:517)

The girls experienced distress at hiding their sexual orientation by continually checking their Facebook profiles to make sure no one had said anything negative about them. One girl was constantly reviewing her account to make sure her parents did not know that she dated a girl. Another girl did not want her parents to know she was a lesbian and decided not to post a picture of her holding hands with her girlfriend. A third girl described how her friends were trying to appear authentic when posting photos on Facebook, but she could not do this as parts of her life were concealed from her peers (Rubin & McCelland, 2015).

One girl reported that if she had feelings for another girl, she would push them to the back of her mind, while another said she felt terrible about not being able to share her feelings on Facebook. A different girl, who was questioning her sexual identity orientation, ended up crying most of the time, as she felt weird and confused when thinking about it (Rubin & McCelland, 2015). Two girls were worried about their personal safety, where one disclosed if she came out online others would say things to her brother, and she said she may get hurt (Rubin & McCelland, 2015).

When these young women access their Facebook accounts it seems like a lot of hard work to conceal their sexual orientation from others that matter to them. They appear to use different strategies to their heterosexual peers who will regularly share their thoughts and feelings on Facebook (Rubin & McCelland, 2015). The way in which these participants manage their accounts presents potential opportunities to experience feelings of depression, anxiety, and shame due to potential offensive comments from others. So, coming out takes on a different meaning on Facebook as by altering their self-presentation to prevent social exclusion, this then becomes a difficult activity (Rubin & McCelland, 2015).

—

By looking at these two studies there is a stark difference in the researchers' findings. The first study revealed that the gay and bisexual young men used chat rooms, message boards, forums, email, IM and blogs to explore their sexual orientation, receive advice from others and to meet other young men. This proved to be a successful way for them to do this.

On the other hand, connections on Facebook are driven by having an audience in mind, with the hope that one can maintain, or increase friendships with people who are compatible. That was not the case for the young lesbians or bisexual women who participated in the second study. This group expressed a fear of being 'outed online', were worried about their personal safety and not being able to explore their sexual orientation. Most of them appear distressed at having to continually review their Facebook accounts to make sure no one has made hurtful comments about them (Rubin & McCelland, 2015). While remaining closeted may temporarily avoid sexual stigma, this strategy can result in the number of places where bisexual or lesbian young women can express themselves and share experiences becoming restricted, rather than expanded through using Facebook (Rubin & McCelland, 2015).

—

Research has consistently found that lesbian, gay and bisexual youth have higher risk of depression, anxiety, and suicide than their heterosexual peers (Rosario et al., 2011) and an increased risk for substance misuse (Darwich et al., 2012). The health risks of experiencing online social exclusion should not be underestimated.

Counselling LGBT Clients

As part of my training to be a counsellor, I worked voluntarily for MESMAC North Yorkshire, where I was responsible for counselling gay and bisexual men (www.mesmac.co.uk). Many were in their late adolescent years and were struggling to come to terms with their sexual orientation. I also counselled lesbians and bisexual young women who were referred to me through a different agency which has now closed.

To help these young people to identify the difficulties that they might encounter when trying to discover their sexual orientation I used exploratory questions in our therapy sessions to help them to talk about any anxieties they may have. I structured the work in four stages: (1) telling their families; (2) telling their friends; (3) being open with colleagues; and (4) being totally open with everyone. All these stages were led by my clients, and different individuals took different amounts of time to go through them. I considered this a safer way to come out than to tell everyone, and then experience rejection from homophobes.

In helping young clients to tell their families I asked questions such as, "What do you want to say to your parents about your sexuality?" and "How will you respond if you get a negative or positive reaction from your parents?" By 'testing' the ground with their parents, if they received a favourable response, many then had the confidence to tell their friends. If a parent's response was negative, such as being shocked, guilty, or in denial, and this did not change with time, then this would affect the young person's ability to move through the other three stages.

Once they had told their families, this invariably gave them the confidence to speak to close friends. I know from personal experience that today's young people who have a problem with the LGBT community are in an increasingly small minority. Nevertheless, one of the hardest things for LGBT young people is to face rejection from their friends. I enquired on the behalf of those who did not have any friends and those who had experienced rejection, if there were any LGBT forums in their schools or local area. This was with a view to encourage them to make new friends.

There is current legislation in the workplace to protect vulnerable adolescents from bullying and discrimination in relation to sexual orientation. Most young people who have come through the first three stages of the model are not unduly worried about coming out to the wider community. New laws in the UK have made our society more equal for the LGBT community, and same-sex couples can now get married and have children.

For some adolescents, when expressing their sexual orientation, it can feel like they are confessing to something that is considered taboo by some members of our society. Therefore, they need to feel supported and valued along the way to being open about their sexual orientation. I have been asked why it is important for members of the LBGT society to feel they must come out, as the heterosexual community do not tell everyone they are heterosexual. I do not think it is important for individuals to express their sexual orientation unless they wish to do so, for example if they want to challenge homophobic individuals. In the same way that some members of the LGBT communities feel the need to come out, there are parents who need to outwardly express that their son or daughter is LGBT. There are many online support networks which parents can access, and I will list them in the guide for parents at the end of this chapter.

Guides for Parents and Teachers

Parents

As a parent you may have concerns about your son or daughter being LGBT. I encourage parents to always be led by your adolescents in how they describe their sexual orientation, and not to dismiss their feelings or experiences at any stage. If you can reassure your adolescent that their identity is genuine and use empathic responses (see the chapter on racism) this will prove immensely helpful. They may need extra support to make good decisions, for example, knowing what their rights are, and where they can access support regarding sexual matters and staying safe.

There are additional risks for young men who have penetrative sex with other young men in that they may generate an increased risk of contracting HIV, the virus that causes AIDS (Garafalo et al., 2007). Using a condom helps to protect against HIV and lowers the risk of getting many other STIs. A survey carried out by Stonewall into gay and bisexual men revealed that a third of them had never had an HIV test and a quarter had not been tested for any STIs. The NHS suggest young gay or bisexual men are advised to have a check-up every six months as some STIs do not have any symptoms. For extra information including how to have safe sex for gay and bisexual young men please access the following NHS website: www.nhs.uk/live-well/sexual-health/sexual-health-for-gay-and-bisexual-men. For young women who have sex with other women the NHS have a lot of information regarding this subject on the same website: www.nhs.uk/live-well/sexual-health/sexual-health-for-lesbian-and-bisexual-women. If you need extra support, then go to www.stonewall.org.uk/help-advice/coming-out/coming-out-advice-and-guidance-parents. On this site Stonewall discuss lots of ways you can support your adolescent as well as taking your feelings into account. Another website for parents who want support for young people who may have gender issues is: youngminds.org.uk/find-help/for-parents/parents-guide-to-support-gender-identity-issues/.

Teachers

Given the lack of same-sex sexual health information provided to LGBT adolescents through school-based sex education programs, online platforms have become a primary source for many to learn about their sexual orientation. Schools could enhance adolescents' learning by providing a culturally appropriate venue for the exploration and subsequent commitment to an integrated sexual orientation identity. In addition, teachers could develop support networks with peers, which may offset the effects of rejection experienced in offline environments as well as online contexts. The Stonewall website has an abundance of material for teachers consisting of e-learning for staff in schools and colleges and providing support to LGBT young people.

7

SEXUAL REFERENCES, SEXTING, OFFLINE AND ONLINE SEXUAL ABUSE

The exploration of sexual identity becomes a critical feature of young people's lives because during this phase they develop a sense of their sexual selves (Buzzwell & Rosenthal, 1996). Physical changes start in early adolescent years (10–13) when young people are overly concerned about their body image. During middle adolescent years (14–16) and late adolescence (17–19) young people develop an interest in sexual exploration (Kar et al., 2015). They begin to seek out information relating to sexual matters and eventually most adolescents become sexually confident in themselves. Social factors play a significant role in the development of adolescent sexuality. The attitude of parents toward sexuality, parenting style, peer relationship, and cultural influences are important factors which facilitate sexual learning and decide the sexual attitudes of their adolescents (Kar et at., 2015).

Sexual Self-Presentation

Social media has become an important tool which young people can use for sexual exploration as well as seeking out sexual information. Adolescents may also produce sexual content by presenting themselves in a sexual way (Shafer et al., 2013). They do this by posting sexual photos often consisting of sexually suggestive poses or semi-naked, for example in swimwear or underwear (Van Oosten et al., 2014). This activity is called sexual self-presentation.

To understand the reasons adolescents post sexual images of themselves, it is important to consider their main audience and how they would like to be seen by them. Generally, they share images of themselves to maintain and increase their peer networks. When adolescents present themselves online in sexy ways, their friends can play an important role as providers of sexual information (Shafer et al., 2013). Positive feedback from their friends is important as it helps young people to reduce any doubts they may have about themselves while developing a sexual self (Shafer et., al 2013). Previous research has shown that adolescents know which type of photos are admired by their friends and by presenting attractive photos, they promote their social acceptance amongst their peer group (Salimkhan et al., 2010). Not only is it important to post attractive photos, but they can also gain popularity among other social media users (Siibak, 2009). One study found that young people are more likely to post sexual images online if they have friends who also post the same type of images (Moreno et al., (2009).

Adolescents' sexual self-presentation

An investigation by Baumgartner, et al., (2015) looked at what type of sexy photos adolescents post online, and how the participants are perceived by their friends.

Self-presentation of 'sexy' photos

The researchers asked this group how likely they were to post three different types of sexual photos online: a sexy photo wearing sexy clothing; photos showing them wearing sexy clothing and posing sexually; and photos in swimwear or underwear.

The results from the participants' responses show that 34 per cent said they are more likely to post a sexy photo of themselves rather than posing sexually (8 per cent), or in swimwear or underwear (5 per cent). These findings suggest that most adolescents want to appear sexually attractive, however, some participants posted photos that were more revealing (Baumgatner et., al. 2015).

Evaluation by peers

To check the adolescents' perception of their peers, the researchers created Facebook profiles for eight girls and eight boys with photos of the profile owners. Two of the Facebook profiles, one boy and one girl, were manipulated to vary their sexual self-presentation by changing their profile photos. The new profile shows the same person in two different poses, non-sexual and sexual. The non-sexual version showed a close-up of their faces, and they were wearing ordinary clothes, whilst the sexual version portrayed them with the upper part of their bodies in swimwear (Baumgartner et al., 2015).

The participants were split into two mixed gender groups. The first group were shown one sexual boy and one non-sexual girl, while the second group were shown one non-sexual boy and one sexual girl. The participants were asked to rate on a scale whether they found the profiles popular or whether they thought they were unpopular.

The results show that girls who assessed the girl that presented herself in a sexual way, evaluated her more negatively than the girls who evaluated the non-sexual girl. There is clearly some jealousy, or moral judgement expressed by the girls. Previous research implies that females are derogatory towards other females who present themselves in sexual ways because they make sexual encounters too available for males (Buss & Schmitt, 1993). This makes it more difficult for females to obtain a partner, because if there is a shortage of males in a community it is the more attractive females who find a mate to reproduce with (Buss & Schmitt,1993). The girls assessed the sexual boy more positively than the girls who assessed the non-sexual boy. This result can be considered alongside Buss and Schmitt's (1993) theory in which they claim that females will be more attracted to strong, attractive, muscular male bodies for mating purposes.

However, earlier research suggests that males do not acknowledge their sexual self-presentation a productive way to attract females (Buss & Schmitt, 1993). This was evident with the boys in this study as they did not differentiate much in their assessment of other boys who presented themselves in sexual or non-sexual ways (Baumgatner et al., 2015). Therefore, a sexual self-presentation of their boy peers may not be perceived as threatening their position amongst the girls, and could also increase boys' popularity both amongst the girls and other boys.

—

This study reports low levels of online sexual self-presentation by both boys and girls. It also identifies how peer influences play a crucial role in deciding whether adolescents post sexual photos of themselves on social media (Baumgartner et al., 2015).

Gender-Based Sexualised Comments

Previous research showed girls' online sexy self-presentations seemed to copy the popularity of female sexualised bodies shown on traditional media sites (Ringrose, 2009). Some of the comments that girls receive from the boys are usually positive ('nice pic', 'good looking' or 'hello sexy'), while others are offensive ('fat slag', 'bitch', or 'whore') (Ringrose, 2011:106).

A study by Masheroni et al., (2015), found that double standards existed between the boys and girls from three different countries when posting sexy images onto their social media sites. The boys distance themselves from the practice of taking selfies as a female trait and claimed that girls take selfies in front of the mirror as though they are celebrities. The boys also reported that girls become addicted to the number of 'likes' they receive. This was articulated by one boy who said that to get more 'likes' for their photos the girls post selfies in which they are semi-naked. A second boy stated that girls may show their breasts or other parts of their body on Twitter, and then say 'Hello' to all the boys to get more followers (Masheroni et al., 2015). The boys explained that girls who post sexy photos of themselves deserve any negative consequences such as being bullied or groomed by strangers. The attitudes by the boys show a total lack of empathy for the girls as they blame the girls for posing sexually in their photos, but they still decide to share these photos with others. This often results in the girls being ridiculed or humiliated online (Masheroni et al., 2015).

Many of the girls reported that they link peer acceptance with the approval of the number of 'likes' they receive, as well as posting photos consistent with beauty standards to avoid being criticised. This was described by one girl who said that no one is interested in her if she does not receive many 'likes'. A second girl explained how one of her peers ended up in hospital after dieting because she was obsessed with having a perfect thigh gap (the visible space between her inner thighs). The girls expressed that the boys do not receive offensive comments about their sexual self-presentation. For instance, one girl said that when a photo is displayed of a boy without a T-shirt or in his underwear, nothing is said, however, it is different if it is a girl posing in underwear. These types of photos displayed by the girl often result in the boys calling them tramps or whores (Masheroni et al., 2015).

The boys claimed when girls decide to be seen in a sexy pose, it is assumed that they are aware of the consequences of their choice. Their decision implies they have accepted responsibility for the social identity they are projecting especially when they know it may be passed to others by people they do not know. Clearly girls are having a hard time – trying to become more popular with their peers, but at the same time running the risk of being criticised. I feel saddened that young girls evaluate their peer worth by posting provocative photos of themselves on Twitter and Facebook, only to be labelled as tramps. These offensive comments may cause long-lasting negative effects such as low self-esteem. This is because psychological concepts are rooted in girls' beauty and appearance (Stuart & Donaghue, 2012) which the girls are trying to promote online.

Sexting

Sexy online self-presentation

Some young people send and receive, or forward, sexual messages, photos, or images of themselves in personal conversations on their mobiles to others in a practice known as 'sexting'. Sexting allows adolescents to behave in a promiscuous manner without doing so in front of another person (Diliberto & Mattey, 2009). But, once their sexual images or messages are sent into cyberspace, there is no way of controlling further distribution.

Van Oosten and Vandenbosh (2017) investigated whether adolescents aged 13–17 years and young adults aged 18–25 years who had been exposed to other's sexy material, were more willing to engage in sexting. The researchers asked the participants how often they had deliberately sought out photos of others in the last two months on their social media sites, with a sexy gaze; with a sexy appearance; in swimwear or underwear; and in a sexy pose (Van Oosten & Vandenbosh, 2017). To assess the participants' willingness to engage in sexting the researchers asked, "Is it likely you would send a photo of yourself or text message of you, naked or almost naked if you were asked by your partner; someone you are dating; a friend; a stranger; or your ex-partner?" (Van Oosten & Vandebosh, 2017:45).

The results indicate that exposure to other's sexy self-presentation on social media predicts the willingness to engage in sexting, but only amongst adolescent girls (Van Oosten & Vandebosh, 2017). Adolescent girls are often taught that sexting may be dangerous and illegal (Chalfen, 2009) and are usually reluctant to engage in this type of behaviour (Dir et al., 2013). However, these negative experiences may be offset by the need to be sexually curious and to increase their popularity amongst their peers (Siibak, 2009). It may also be that the adolescent girls' sexting behaviour can be motivated by self-expression, which is in line with society's messages that girls receive about the importance of looking sexy and attractive (Tolman, 2002). The female young adults did not show the same willingness to text. The discrepancy between this group and the adolescent girls may be down to age differences and the conformity to engage in sexting.

Exposure to other's sexy self-presentation and the willingness to text by the boys and young adult males revealed that the boys had a significantly higher willingness to sext than the adolescent girls. This suggests that the adolescent boys did not feel stigmatised about sexting and their motivations appear different to the adolescent girls. Their sexting behaviour may be led by sexual desire and society's expectations to act on sexual impulses (Van Oosten & Vandebosh, 2017). While sexting is often intended as a private activity, the possibility of sexually explicit photos being posted to an unintended, large audience may make such sexual behaviours problematic (Diliberto & Matttey, 2009), with implications such as breaking the law.

Offline Sexual Abuse

Views on sexting behaviour need to be considered in the light of legal perspectives, where sexting is considered illegal and a form of child pornography (Chalfen, 2009) which may lead to inappropriate offline meetings and sexual abuse. Many of us are aware of individuals coming forward to report the sexual abuse they experienced as young children such as the heinous abuse committed by the late Jimmy Saville. There have also been recent reports into the sexual abuse of young male footballers, and the biggest investigation into abuse of an estimated 1400 adolescent girls, which took place in Rotherham during 1997–2013.

In the UK, child abuse is defined as 'forcing or enticing a child or young person to take part in sexual activities, not necessarily involving a high level of violence, whether or not the child or young person is aware of what is happening. The activities may involve physical contact, including assault by penetration for example, rape or oral sex, or non-penetrative acts such as masturbation, kissing, rubbing, and touching outside of clothing. They can include non-contact activities, such as involving children or young people in looking at, or in the production of, sexual images, watching sexual activities, encouraging children to behave in sexually inappropriate ways, or grooming a child in preparation for abuse including via the internet.' (www. www.gov.uk/goverment/ publications).

As a counsellor, I learnt that childhood sexual abuse occurs across many different class structures and often continues until the child is approaching puberty. Gone are the days when the perpetrators were perceived as sleazy old men in raincoats. Many sexual perpetrators, both women and men, are from all walks of life, and some of them hold responsible positions. I have had male and female former clients who have named social workers, teachers, psychiatrists, police officers, a judge, and grandparents committing sexual abuse to satisfy their own needs.

About a third of child sexual abuse is carried out by older children or young people, while nine out of ten children know or are related to their abuser. The abuse can take place anywhere. Sexual perpetrators lure their victims with a process called grooming, which involves building an emotional connection with a child to gain their trust for the purposes of sexual abuse, sexual exploitation, or trafficking. Much of the abuse starts when a child is too young to know that it is wrong for an adult to abuse them in that way. Some of the signs that a child or adolescent is being abused are:

- They may become aggressive, withdrawn, not sleeping or revert to bed wetting.
- They may dislike or seem afraid of the abuser.
- They may behave in a sexually inappropriate way or use inappropriate language.
- They may have soreness in the genital or anal areas or have a sexual disease.
- They may have difficulty concentrating and learning at school.
- They may drop hints that the abuse is happening without revealing it outright.

The ramifications of sexual abuse can be far reaching and cause individuals to feel ashamed and guilty, even though it was not their fault. They may also struggle with managing their emotions, trusting others, and experience feelings of inadequacy holding them back in school or working life. Some individuals develop mental health problems in later life, including depression, anxiety and eating disorders, while most struggle with education or getting a job. Many people have difficulties with relationships, avoiding sexual intimacy, while others have multiple sexual partners. They are more likely to self-harm, become involved in criminal behaviour, misuse drugs and alcohol, and to commit suicide as young adults. It took a long time, sometimes up to two years, for my clients to realise they were valued, that the abuse was not their fault, and they could leave our counselling relationship with their heads held high. It is also important for readers to know that not all people who have been sexually abused will have problems later in life. Some individuals will reconcile their past by themselves and mature into well-adjusted adults.

Online Sexual Abuse

There is evidence that childhood sexual abuse is increasing online because social media, chat rooms and forums are all used by child sex abusers to groom potential victims (Noll et al., 2009). These sites can connect perpetrators to young people very easily, and at the same time allow the perpetrators to remain anonymous. Also, the wide use of social media has created increased opportunities for perpetrators to initiate contact with adolescents to set up offline sexual encounters. Abuse may not be directly associated with offline encounters, but via an indirect pathway. For example, adolescent girls who present themselves in a provocative manner may increase their vulnerability for social media victimisation. However, both boys and girls may not have sufficient experience in deterring advances from perpetrators online and in potential offline face-to-face encounters.

Posting sexual photos of oneself may prove dangerous as it can lead to unwanted sexual invitations (Mitchell, 2007) and has been related to risky offline sexual behaviour (Bobkowski et al., 2012). Young adolescents may not realise that offline encounters may result in them being victims of sexual assault or even rape. Some individuals who commit these offences may think the only consequences will be involvement with the police, and the worst-case scenario going to prison. However, there are many more potential consequences for them. The families of the perpetrators must live with the shame, and the victims' families may feel guilty about not being able to protect them. The victims can suffer trauma, depression, anxiety, and post-traumatic stress disorder (PTSD) following a sexual assault or rape.

Protecting Adolescents from Online Perpetrators

Parents

I encourage parents to become more knowledgeable of their adolescents' behaviours, attitudes, and peer affiliations that are associated with online sexual invitations and offline meetings. Talk to your young person about how online sexual self-presentation can influence the behaviours and perceptions of others. Discourage the sharing of personal information, and discuss the dangers associated with talking about sex with strangers. Explore options for filtering, blocking, and monitoring adolescents' social media usage. Posting and viewing sexual material and sexting remains a serious issue and will not be controlled without vigilance and education from parents and schools. I have adopted the advice given by Diliberto and Mattey (2009) to reduce the risks attached to sexting. I think their recommendations should apply to all sexual images that adolescents post on their social media sites.

Think about the consequences

Advise adolescents to think before sending a sexual image of someone who is underage (currently aged under sixteen years) even if it is of themselves. They could face humiliation or risk legal sanctions.

Never take images they would not want to share

One of the most helpful tips for parents in advising their adolescents on sexting is to teach them to follow the phrase 'WWGT' ('What Would Grandma Think?'). If they do not want their grandma to see their messages, they should not send them (kidshealth.org/en/parents/2011-sexting.html).

Before hitting the send button

Tell them they cannot control where their images and messages will travel. If they send it to a friend it may end up with their friends, and then their friends, and so forth.

Forwarding sexy pictures

Advise them that if they forward a sexy picture of someone underage, they are responsible as the sender, and may face child pornography charges or may even have to register as a sex offender.

Report nude pictures

Ask them to report any nude photos they receive on their mobiles, either to yourself or to another adult that they can trust, and do not delete the image or messages. Once they have done this, encourage them to block the user who sent the explicit image.

—

You can talk directly to the police or your local children's social services anonymously if you want to report an incident of abuse, or get further advice by phoning the NSPCC's free helpline on 0808 800 5000 (www.nspcc.org.uk). If you are an adolescent and someone is sexually abusing you, you can get support from Childline by calling free on 0800 1111 (www. childline.org.uk). All calls are confidential.

Teachers

Reacting to normal urges and curiosities about sex is a large part of adolescents' developing sexual identity. However, social media may not be the healthiest or safest avenue in which to explore these issues. Insights into current sexual behaviours could be developed by schools for supporting young people as they learn to manage their sexual self-presentation on social media. Respectful interactions amongst boys and girls should be taught along with an awareness of the double standards that may exist concerning their sexual reputation, particularly what the willingness to sext can mean for adolescent girls in terms of positive and negative consequences for their sexuality.

8

MEDIA REFERENCES TO ALCOHOL AND IMPACT ON ALCOHOL CONSUMPTION

Young people have a greater vulnerability towards alcohol consumption than adults because they are physically smaller and do not have sufficient knowledge of what constitutes a safe amount of alcohol to consume (Anderson et al., 2009). In 2009 the Chief Medical Officer of England published a report containing guidance for alcohol consumption for young people (www.gov.uk/government/consultations/alcohol-strategy-consultation). The report recommends that the safest way for young people to drink is to refrain from drinking alcohol until they reach the age of eighteen years. For those who do drink alcohol the report suggests that the lower age group should not be younger than fifteen and they should only drink once a week in a supervised environment.

Adolescents are often encouraged to start drinking by observing others and modelling their behaviour in social environments. This behaviour is typical of social learning theory (Bandura, 1977). New learning may happen without an immediate change in behaviour, but happens gradually, when it affects the attitudes and the consequences of how individuals act. An important social learning principle of how people behave under the influence of alcohol is social norms in which individuals replicate the behaviour of significant others (peers, parents, and role models). They use these people as guides to normal drinking practices, and imitating others reinforces socially acceptable behaviour. However, individuals are likely to overestimate the amount of alcohol consumed by others and these false perceptions can have an influence on personal drinking consumption. This influence is further compounded by the belief, whether it seems right or wrong, that these others approve of this type of behaviour (Berkowtz, 2005).

Peers are particularly important to model alcohol references of attitudes and behaviour as they share stories with each other about themselves with one story that is especially common, a 'drunken narrative' (Griffin et al., 2009). Sharing stories about drinking episodes is part of young people's drinking culture and plays a significant role in friendship dynamics (MacLean, 2016). Adolescents who drink alcohol may be perceived as sharing social practices, and this is linked to having fun with close friends.

Social Media and Alcohol Advertising

Alcohol advertising is one of the many factors that can potentially encourage young people to start or continue to drink alcohol (Anderson et al., 2009). Advertisements are spread across a wide range of media, and research suggests different adverts play an important role in shaping and understanding normal and acceptable drinking practices (Velleman, 2009; Moreira & Foxcroft, 2010). Adolescents frequently post alcohol images on social media to be socially accepted, and to associate with a peer group that enjoys drinking and partying (Moreno et al., 2009). Online alcohol images also embellish and memorialise heavy drinking sessions, and the comments and encouragement of their peers can result in additional pleasure for the users (Brown & Gregg, 2012).

However, there are risks to posting alcoholic images. On social media such images are an exact replica of real-life events, and when shared publicly, they become available to a vast audience in seconds. Publicly owning their drinking habits can increase criticism from parents, especially if the posts are from those aged under eighteen.

Adolescents' Interpretation of Alcoholic Images

A report carried out by Atkinson et al. (2011) explored how alcohol images are represented in the media and in what way adolescents aged 11–18 years interpret how these images are characterised. Although their report covers all media, that is, TV programmes, magazines, I will focus on the influence of social media on alcohol references and consumption of alcohol (www.ias.org.uk).

The researchers examined websites using a list of leading alcohol brands to gain insight into the range of alcohol advertising. They discovered that social media was used by alcohol producers or distributors to display alcohol content advertising. They identified the leading brands in the UK who advertise their products online and their marketing strategies. These consist of promotion of offline branded events at a club or sporting event, interactive games, sponsored online events, and invitations to drink (Atkinson et al., 2011).

Social media presents new environments for alcohol

advertisers to reach their target market because they can direct their promotional material to specific people. The researchers identified two types of alcohol references that appear on these sites. They are 'official references' which consist of images, or pictures of brands generated by the alcohol producer or distributor, and 'unofficial references' which include images, pictures of brands, or pictures of oneself all created by the user (Atkinson et al., 2011). Both types of references appear on platforms such as, Facebook, Myspace and YouTube.

Official alcohol advertising

Social media sites

On social media sites the researchers found that most alcohol producers were abiding by the Advertising Standards Agency (ASA) regulations instructing that reference to responsible drinking had a presence on their websites. For example, some advertisers displayed a reference to Drinkaware (www.drinkaware.co.uk) and Talk to Frank (www.talktofrank.com), two government-funded campaigns that include advice and support for underage drinkers and their parents. Many leading brands also had official Facebook pages, in which they were able to promote and advertise their products. The researchers found that these pages differed slightly in that not all referred to responsible drinking, but they all excluded images of what might appear to be underage drinking (Atkinson et al., 2011).

YouTube

On YouTube, I accessed a popular song called 'Da Tweekaz – Jägermeister Official Video' (www.Jägermeister.com), which featured in the researchers' list of YouTube websites. The producers had incorporated an Austrian-Bavarian yodel into their music. The theme of this video shows three young men having a great time, while the setting consists of an energetic party atmosphere. Below are some of the comments which feature on this website:

- The best product placement I'll ever see.
- I started drinking Jägermeister because of this song.
- This song reminds me of the 7 dwarfs who sing a yodelling song. I love it.
- Can't wait until I'm 18 then I'll be able to drink a Jägermeister.
- Jägermeister is awesome, it has everything, the taste, the beautiful logo and the bottle.
- This is my everyday song cos everything works together. It's excellent.

These are examples where video advertising encourages people to start drinking. Although there was a small reference to 'drinking responsibly' at the foot of the page, this link did not direct me to Drinkaware or Talk to Frank. Instead, it outlined Jägermeister's marketing code and principles, and was aimed at adults over the age of eighteen, stating that they are responsible for their actions.

Unofficial alcohol advertising

Atkinson et al. (2011) identified that social media sites and YouTube also provide opportunities for young people to promote their drinking culture through their own advertising.

Social media sites

The results showed that some adolescents created unofficial content on Facebook by posting drinking-related photos, and advertising alcohol brands. These unofficial pages omit any reference to responsible drinking and openly present alcohol brands, logos and links to official brand websites and drunkenness in a positive and jubilant manner (Atkinson et al., 2011). The pages also included playing interactive games relating to alcohol. For example, one game allowed users to pass a 'virtual' drink to their peers who appeared on their social media sites (Atkinson et al., 2011). Adolescents participating in this study who were aged under thirteen had social media profiles despite the fact these accounts should not be set up by those younger than thirteen.

YouTube

YouTube users also presented their own remakes of official alcohol advertisements such as WKD robot advert, Do the Lambrini, as well as posting humorous comments on the official campaign pages. Videos also depicted individuals drinking specific alcohol brands (WKD) and participating in drinking games (AfterShock, Jägermeister). Overall, responsible drinking information was less prominent with the unofficial adverts.

—

It is my belief that some young people who create their own online unofficial advertising may be experiencing a 'fear of missing out' (FoMO). This is described by Davis (2012) as a worry that individuals are excluded from something important, like fun activities. The need to belong to a peer group which is associated with having fun is paramount in young people's minds. Given that people with high levels of FoMO are more sensitive about their social bonds it seems reasonable that they may turn to social media including YouTube to seek relationships with others who are having a good time.

This type of public display may attract those adolescents who want to achieve celebrity status. Benn (2017), when studying identity development, claims that many young people want to be famous, and they accomplish this by putting homemade videos of themselves on YouTube. Before the advent of YouTube, it was difficult to claim fame through traditional forms of media such as TV, magazines or movies. Nowadays online fame is quickly reached by using this platform. Whilst it may seem far-fetched to think that adolescents will be famous overnight by uploading a YouTube video of themselves, some have proved successful (Benn, 2017).

Drinking frequency

Atkinson et al., (2011) asked their group of adolescents to complete a questionnaire to determine their drinking frequency and their friends' perceived drinking consumption. The average age was just over fourteen years, with 84.2 per cent stating they had drunk alcohol, while gender was evenly spread with 55.2 per cent of males and 44.8 per cent of females reporting they had drunk alcohol (Atkinson et al., 2011).

The result shows that overall, adolescents felt that their friends consume more alcohol (16.4 percent) than themselves (8 percent) but only when they compared their drinking habits to their friends once a week. When the researchers broke down the age groups, they found that the estimation of friends' drinking was similar in younger age groups to that of the participant, but older respondents tended to believe that their friends drank more than they did. The researchers also identified that the more the participants thought their friends drank, the more they consumed themselves (Atkinson et al., 2011).

Attitudes to drinking

When asked about the attitudes of others and their drinking habits, some younger adolescents felt that their friends would want them to drink less or stop drinking. They also reported the main influence on them to start drinking was peer pressure from their friends (Atkinson et al., 2011). A higher percentage of older participants believed their friends would encourage them to drink more and be less likely to inform authority figures. The older adolescents also thought teachers and parents would find it acceptable for them to drink, but they did not care what other adults thought (Atkinson et al., 2011).

This group of participants reported regularly viewing online alcohol advertising from a variety of brands, particularly when logging into sites such as Facebook. They also recalled having viewed alcohol advertisements on football team websites, YouTube and 'pop-ups' on non-alcohol related websites. Older adolescents mentioned how they had seen images of themselves enjoying a night out with their friends drinking alcohol on social media sites.

When asked why they did this, they suggested that uploading drinking photographs was a way of portraying an image of themselves, for example, 'mad', 'cool', 'fun' and 'hard' (Atkinson et al., 2011). However, most of this group were reluctant to openly discuss uploading images of themselves drinking and spoke negatively about others who did, by saying they were dumb or stupid (Atkinson et al., 2011).

Alcohol Images on Facebook, Myspace and YouTube

A second study carried out by Morgan et al. (2010) examined young students' use of social media through posting public images of themselves drinking alcohol and behaving in an inebriated manner. On Facebook and Myspace, the researchers found that 68 per cent of this group currently consumed alcohol, with 32 per cent drinking alcohol once a week, and 23 per cent reporting that they drink once a month.

The participants were also asked how many images they had taken of themselves on their own, with their friends, and ones of just their friends were posted on either Facebook or Myspace. The results showed that 83 per cent posted images of their friends, with 38 per cent posting images of the participant and only 32 per cent posting images of themselves. Not surprisingly the majority posted images of mixed gender friends alone and in groups rather than themselves drinking hard spirits, beer, or wine, and displaying drunken behaviour (Morgan et al., 2010). This could be a way to avoid getting into trouble while still creating a party atmosphere on their social media sites.

YouTube

Eighteen per cent of participants reported posting a video, with 10 per cent posting one of themselves, and only two people posting one of friends. The videos included individuals engaged in behaviours with known effects of drinking too much alcohol such as slurred speech, lack of muscle coordination, poor judgment, loss of inhibition, and vomiting (Morgan et al., 2010). Other actions included people drinking from bottles, saying that these people were drunk, and playing pranks on someone else they described as drunk (Morgan et al., 2010). There was also evidence that the videos are being viewed frequently, and they are commented on by an audience of YouTube members. There appears to be much less involvement in making videos of alcohol consumption than there are images appearing on Myspace or Facebook. This could be because Myspace and Facebook have a higher degree of privacy and adolescents who use these sites may control their audiences in a more satisfactory way.

Attitudes about drinking alcohol

Nearly all the participants reported they are aware of other people posting images of themselves drinking alcohol, with just over half reporting posting pictures of themselves. While 50 per cent of this group indicated that while it might seem 'stupid' or 'dumb', it was the right of the individual to decide. For example, one participant explained, he did not care, although he thought it was stupid, but people can post whatever images they want. Just over a quarter of the participants pointed out there was no problem with posting images portraying alcohol use and that it can be funny or indicate social group membership. Other results revealed that students' attitudes towards alcohol images suggested accepting attitudes towards this behaviour, primarily not endorsing the behaviour for themselves, but noting that it is okay for others to do so (Morgan, et al., 2010).

—

A combination of these two studies identifies that peer acceptance, and perceptions of friends' drinking habits appear to encourage young people to start drinking and continue to post online alcohol images. The evidence shows that the main motive is to enjoy themselves and appear cool. The results also show that participants thought their peers consumed more than themselves, and both studies identified a 'couldn't-care-less' attitude towards the opinions of others except their friends. There is an opportunity to interact with their friends online, and to minimise the experience of FoMO. This is further evidence of young people trying to construct an online self in relation to their peers, so that they can be part of the 'collective' group identity.

Early consumption of alcohol is determined partly by the alcohol use of adolescent friends as well as by social network characteristics (Mundt, 2011). Adolescents who view alcohol references on their peers' Facebook profiles find these to be believable and are influential sources of information (Morena, et al., 2009). Furthermore, young people who perceive alcohol use as normal on Facebook profiles are more likely to report an interest in beginning alcohol use (Litt & Stock, 2011). Consequently, social media represents a readily available, and consistently accessed, source of information for today's young people by combining the power of interpersonal persuasion with the reach of mass media.

Potential Health Risks

Throughout adolescence their brains continue to grow and

change as the synapses that connect all the different neurons become more complex and efficient. Excessive drinking throughout this stage may alter this process and can result in them having potential brain damage. One part of the brain that is affected by alcohol is the hippocampus which is responsible for learning and memory (De Bellis et al., 2000), and drinking at high levels can permanently impair brain development (Spear, 2002). Damage to this part of the brain may include how well adolescents do at school, at work, in hobbies and learning new skills like driving a car. The front part of the brain, called the pre-frontal cortex, matures during adolescence, and plays a role in reasoning, planning, problem-solving, consideration for others, and self-control. Excessive drinking can cause it to deteriorate and not develop normally which leads to individuals becoming irrational, overly confident or less inhibited.

Drinking by adolescents is also connected to car crash injury and death, suicide and depression, cirrhosis of the liver, loss of memory, broken friendships, date rape, and unprotected sexual intercourse which places young people at risk for sexually transmitted disease, HIV infection and unplanned pregnancies (Bonomo et al., 2001).

Guides for Parents and Teachers

Parents

Parents need to be aware of the dangers that may occur, particularly the health and legal implications for their young people who are posting references to alcohol online. If you notice a reference to alcohol use on your adolescent's social media site or see a video of them drinking on YouTube, that is a good time to discuss safe drinking. On the Drinkaware site there is a self-assessment questionnaire that young people can fill in to determine whether they need help to cut down or stop drinking. I would encourage parents to read this website as well as utilizing Talk to Frank, another agency, as a starting point for discussion. If you are really worried about your adolescent's drinking behaviour and their safety, then refer them to your GP. I realise it is difficult to find a balance between you being a 'party pooper' and allowing them some independence.

If your adolescents are already drinking, you can encourage them to drink safely by advising them to eat before they drink, drink slowly, and substitute a non-alcoholic drink every other drink, to become aware of unfamiliar drinks, stay with their friends and get taxis home. Make sure they know about the legal implications of drinking underage, driving whilst drunk, and familiarise them with their school or college policies regarding alcohol misuse. Talk to them about their privacy rights and the implications of drunken behaviour being seen by a future college or employer. For online images that are of concern tell them references to drinking can be incriminating for those under the legal drinking age of eighteen years in the UK.

Teachers

Understanding to what extent teachers, colleges, and other influential adults are privy to young people's displays of alcohol content on social media is an area for future inquiry. Sixty per cent of college students report difficulties online with their alcohol use (Ridout et al., 2012). This high-risk behaviour online adds to the already daunting challenges that counsellors face in tackling alcohol misuse in colleges, and the use of social media to screen students for alcohol-related issues may have an adverse effect.

One study investigating students' preferred means of communication found they felt uncomfortable having an unknown person screen their social media sites and described having a stranger screening their Facebook pages for signs of depression as 'creepy' (Whitehill et al., 2013). In another study most students agreed when they viewed alcohol content displayed on social media it was perceived as suggestive of alcohol use. They also said they would prefer to be approached in a direct manner by someone they knew, as both the relationship with the person and their approach to discussing any problems are key factors in dealing with alcohol misuse (Morena et al., 2012).

—

This chapter aims to provide a snapshot of the influence of alcohol advertising on social media sites about adolescent drinking. If I cast my mind back to mid-1990s when my two daughters were going through a similar stage, they wanted to have a good time and drinking was part of this. I do not think much has changed except today's youth can interact in drinking stories online with their friends, even if they are not at the event in person. This may encourage today's adolescents to start drinking earlier because of increased peer pressure. The additional risks such as drug misuse, date rape, unwanted pregnancy and violence associated with excessive drinking are more obvious than they were during the 1990s, so parents need to be attentive about their young person's drinking habits.

9

SELF-HARM AND SUICIDE

Self-harm and suicide are major public health problems in adolescents, with rates of self-harm increasing during the adolescence phase, and suicide being the second most common cause of death in young people worldwide (Hawton et al., 2012). There is growing concern that social media is perpetuating the risks of self-harm and suicide among vulnerable young people (Farok & Mahmud, 2020). Contributing to these risks are the roles of forums and general internet sites who sometimes indirectly or directly encourage users to carry out this destructive behaviour, instead of seeking help from a GP.

Young people who are marginalised, for example those who have been abused, or affected by sexual exploitation, social exclusion and bullying, may be more at risk of these negative effects. As some of these adolescents have mental health issues, by using social media this may put them in a dangerous situation. They are more likely to be persuaded by others online who may not have the necessary qualifications, as well as having fewer role models demonstrating effective coping strategies. This chapter explores the effects of forums and internet sites on self-harm and suicide, as well as offering guidance on how to support your sons or daughters who may be resorting to this type of behaviour to manage their overwhelming feelings.

Self-Harm

Becoming an adolescent can produce high levels of stress, including developmental and academic pressures, and some may resort to self-harm to manage these issues. Self-harm is described as a deliberate self-injury such as cutting and burning oneself, which usually starts and becomes most frequent between the ages of thirteen and fifteen years, particularly in girls (Rodham & Hawton, 2009). Young people who have depression or anxiety may also know others who use self-harming techniques, and these factors have been identified as an increased risk in several studies (Mitchell et al., 2014).

In most cases, self-harm is generally carried out in a secretive manner and, in many cases, it is not reported because the individual feels ashamed. This makes it difficult to accurately assess how many young people have this mental health issue. However, self-harm amongst adolescents is on the increase in the UK. Kat Lay, health correspondent for the *Sunday Times*, reported that hospital admissions for girls in the UK who self-harmed had doubled from 20 years ago, increasing from 7327 in 1997 to 13,463 in 2017 (www.the times.co.uk). Admissions of boys for self-harm stayed broadly the same from 2,236 in 1997 to 2,332 in 2017. Charities are warning about the pressures social media and schoolwork are putting on young people, and more needs to be done to prevent young people reaching crisis point.

Causes of Self-Harm

Although the reasons for self-harm are complex, research shows adolescents who indicated harming themselves reported significantly increased antisocial behaviour, emotional distress, anger problems, health risk behaviours, and decreased self-esteem (Laye-Gindu & Schonert-Reichl, 2005). People generally feel better after they have self-harmed, because it releases a tension, which then generates a way of managing harmful thoughts and feelings.

The Influence of Forums and Internet Sites on Self-Harm

Daine at al. (2013) carried out a systematic review to establish the influence of forums and internet sites on self-harming behaviour in young people. Some of the studies she investigated showed positive influences, while others presented negative effects.

Forums

Posts reviewed in one study were linked to a reduction of distress by some participants in the third month of posting (Barak & Dolev-Cohen, 2006). In another study participants received praise from others for stopping cutting themselves and for getting help from a GP (Smithson et al., 2011) and the anonymous setting of forums was advantageous for some of its users (Daine et al., 2013). In other studies safety and empathy were frequently mentioned, however the discussions surrounding self-harm were normalised, and did not include preventative measures on how to decrease self-harming behaviour (Smithson et al., 2011). Approximately nine per cent of the total posts were equated to an unhelpful attitude by saying self-harm should be concealed and not disclosed to others (Whitlock et al., 2006).

Internet sites

Daine et al., (2013) found that young people who self-harm may be using internet sites to connect with others, and this may reduce their psychological distress (Mitchell & Ybarra, 2007). However, they also identified that adolescents who self-harm use the internet more than those who do not (Mitchell & Ybarra, 2007), and serious addiction was connected to an increased risk for self-harm (Lam et al., 2009). In another study it was reported that cyber-bullying could have a significant influence on self-harming behaviour (Hay & Meldrum, 2010). Of the eighty per cent of participants from a different study who had been exposed to online suicide or self-harm material, nearly three quarters of them had carried out violent acts on themselves (Collings et al., 2011).

—

Daine's et al., (2013) results suggest some users of online forums perceive them as helpful communities that provide a means of support and coping. However, the use of forums can precipitate self-harm by dissuading the user from seeking professional help. They also identified that the participants reported in their review found that more knowledge can be gained from forums than from internet sites (Daine et al., 2013).

Adam's research into the influence of forums and internet sites on self-harm

Given that Daine's (2013) results are conflicting, I decided to carry out my own research and Googled the following, 'I feel like cutting myself'. From the ten sites I observed, six came up as forums while the rest were internet sites. I found the following information.

Forums

One forum was managed by someone with a PhD, one was led by a counsellor who was not registered, and the rest were run by volunteers. Many of them did not name a trained psychologist, counsellor, or mental health worker on their team. Most of the content consisted of messages from people who had self-harmed but only two of them suggested seeing a therapist. Some of the most unhelpful comments are listed below which I have paraphrased.

- I've had the urge to cut myself. If you want to cut yourself, just cut yourself for a little while, and do what you want. You might think this advice is stupid, who cares!
- Almost everyone self-harms. Sometimes it's even a good thing to self-harm.
- Wake up to your actual feelings, talk about it, and turn to God.

A vulnerable young person reading these sorts of comments may think it is okay to continue cutting themselves, as they will be saved by a divine power. If this was not bad enough, one of the forums was asking readers to volunteer to help others online, without checking for any professional qualifications. I did not find anything on these sites that would constitute a positive influence for someone who was self-harming.

Internet sites

I discovered the NHS website had helpful advice as well as recommending other useful agencies (www.nhs.uk/conditions/self-harm/). Another site hosted by a person holding a PhD offered good advice, but I fear the language she used was too technical for adolescents to understand. The remainder were run by volunteers, many of whom did not have any suitable qualifications, and there were only two which explained specifically who their team consisted of. Most of the content on these sites offers a description of what self-harming is and, sometimes inappropriate, advice on how to stop this happening. One site aimed at adolescents had a list of over a hundred suggestions that an individual could do instead of self-harming. Two of the most ridiculous were, 'Put false tattoos on your skin, look towards the moon and analyse it', and 'tidy your linen cupboard up and re-label it'. Again, I did not find anything on the sites that could be considered as helpful advice.

My experience of accessing online forums and internet sites was unhelpful and unsafe. My research would be more akin to the general user as I was not looking for scholarly articles, just whatever came up. I would not recommend that adolescents who self-harm use these sites without a responsible adult checking their credibility. Compare these sites to the NHS site on self-harm and there is a big difference; they recommend that users should always ask a GP for advice.

Guides for Parents and Teachers

Parents

I suggest that parents look up the online forum and self-harm sites for themselves if they think their sons or daughters are self-harming.

Warning signs of self-harm
Signs to look out for if you think your young person is self-harming may include the following:

- Low mood.
- A change in appetite, overeating or undereating.
- A change in sleeping patterns.
- A need to overdress in hot weather.
- Spots of blood on clothing.
- Unexplained cuts, bruises or burns, often on the wrists, arms, thighs and chest.
- Refusing to get changed in front of other people.

Support mechanisms
One of the best ways to support your sons or daughters is to create a relationship that makes them feel safe enough to talk about their feelings. Be as open as you can and remember they may feel ashamed or worried about your reaction. By remaining calm and not judging what they share, this will help them to feel safe enough to discuss their situation. A conversation needs to be handled in a sensitive manner and you should avoid asking why they self-harm. Most adolescents do not know the answer, and as self-harming behaviour is often misunderstood, they may feel stigmatised if you persist to ask why.

Let them know that you have noticed they appear upset or withdrawn and say something like, "I can see you are upset, and things are difficult for you right now. I am here for you if you want to talk to me. We can try and work this out together". Some other comments listed below can be unhelpful for young people to hear, while others in italics are empathic and can be perceived as validating of their current experience.

- You're the only one who feels that way. vs. *I can understand why you feel like that.*
- It can't be that bad. vs. *It sounds like that's a lot to deal with.*
- There's no reason to get upset. vs. *That must really hurt.*

On the practical side, remove items from your home such as razor blades, pencil sharpeners and scissors that could be used for self-harm. Ensure all medications are kept in a locked cabinet.

Self-harming when alone

Some adolescents choose to self-harm away from home and I recommend you make sure to keep your sons and daughters as safe as possible by giving them a first aid kit and discuss ways of cleaning and covering any cuts, and at the same time look for signs of infection. If your son or daughter is alone when they want to self-harm, help them to practise healthy coping strategies when there are early signs they are becoming distressed such as:

- Listening to loud music.

- Writing a poem.
- Expressing their feelings through art, then changing it to make it less threatening.
- Stroking a pet.
- Watching a film – a funny one or a scary one – to change their emotions.
- Going for a walk with a relative or friend or a pet.
- Talking to someone who makes them laugh.

Try to minimise their self-harming behaviour by helping them to think about what it is that triggers these thoughts and feelings. Ask them to consider other positive coping skills they can use to alleviate their distress.

Self-harming when at home

If they feel the need to self-harm at home, ask them if there is a signal that they may be willing to give you before the self-harming happens. For example, giving you a note or asking you to partake in a specific form of distraction. Young people sometimes find this easier than vocalising how they are feeling. Ask them how they want you to react if they give you this signal. It may be sufficient to take your dog for a walk or watch television which might be enough for them to feel soothed and prevent self-harming behaviour. If your son or daughter does not want to talk to you about what is going on, ask for ideas about who else they could speak to instead. A study into adolescents' views of preventing self-harm reported that the participants considered family, friends, and school as the main sources of support in stopping self-harming behaviour, and more helpful than approaching external helping agencies (Fortune et al., 2008).

Agencies and professional support

Sometimes you will need extra support. If you feel this way, explain to your young person that you want to help, but may not know the best thing to do. Try to come up with a solution together, for example visiting the GP, or seeing a school counsellor. If your son or daughter is not comfortable seeing someone face to face, suggest phoning one of the reputable national agencies once you have researched their credibility. The charity Young Minds (youngminds.org.uk) provides trained volunteers to support young people in crisis by texting YM to 85258. They also have a helpline for parents, 0808 802 5544. Check out the local counselling services in your area. There is also a young person's agency for people aged from 16–25 years run by Mind, the national mental health charity, which offers free counselling (www.mind.org.uk).

Self-harming adolescents may require professional support to address their difficulties and will not be able to stop just because you have found evidence of their behaviour. In this instance parents should take their adolescents to their GP where he or she may make a referral to the local CAMHS unit (child and adolescent mental health service). Do bear in mind that there is usually a long wait for this service. An alternative source of support is private treatment, through contacting The British Association for Counselling and Psychotherapy (www.bacp.co.uk). In the meantime, whilst waiting for someone more specialised to become available, a GP may prescribe anti-depressants to help reduce your adolescent's depression and anxieties if they display these symptoms. I suggest you read my advice in Chapter 3 for being supportive when this type of mental illness occurs.

Teachers

I recommend that teachers read a guide published by *Wiltshire Children's & Young People's Trust* (www.safeguardinginschools. co.uk). This publication outlines how to identify and assess self-harm, and the procedures for dealing with these incidents. This guide should be read in conjunction with other relevant guidelines currently in place at your school or college.

Suicide

May Bulman, Social Affairs Correspondent of the *Independent* newspaper, reports that suicide amongst adolescents is on the increase in England and Wales, with an increase of 67 per cent between 2010 and 2017. But, more worrying, she also quotes figures from the Office of National Statistics (ONS) which states that in the last year alone (2018) 187 under 19s took their own lives, compared with 162 the year before – a rise of 15 per cent (www.independent.co.uk).

Social media has received considerable attention for its role in contributing to suicide ideation (thinking and planning) mainly with young people (Becker et al., 2004). There is also a concern that suicide pacts originating from social media is contagious in the same way that infectious diseases are spread, and that attempted suicide may facilitate the occurrence of this behaviour (Haw et al., 2013).

Abrutyn and Mueller (2014), when researching if the act of suicide was contagious amongst adolescents, found that the impact of suicidal behaviour amongst their participants appears to be more likely when a method of suicide is described. They claimed details of the method being presented especially if it was shown in detail or reported dramatically also increased the risk. A further study by Hawton and Williams (2002) identified that a role model's suicide attempts do in fact trigger new suicidal thoughts amongst vulnerable young people. They found these effects fade with time, but girls are more vulnerable than boys, and the relationship with role models do matter. Peers appear to be more important role models for boys and girls, and their research also states that exposure to suicidal behaviours in significant others may teach other adolescents new ways to deal with emotional distress, i.e. by becoming suicidal (Hawton & Williams, 2002).

Causes of Suicide

Important contributors to suicidal ideation include genetic vulnerability, and psychiatric, psychological, family, social, and cultural factors (Hawton et al., 2012). A recent study by Kim (2020) investigated the major stress-causing factors relating to suicidal ideation and suicide attempts amongst a large group of adolescents by means of a self-reported questionnaire. Schoolwork and career were the most predominant stress factors followed by conflict with peers, and family circumstances. A history of depression was associated in the stressor for conflict with peers.

Many psychiatrists, psychologists, and therapists will diagnose a precursor of suicidal ideation to a history of drug and alcohol misuse, depression, anxiety, or other psychiatric disorders such as eating disorders, schizophrenia, and personality and borderline personalities (Gask, 2000). However, many other factors need to be considered. Life events can act as triggers, for example, loss of a loved one, feeling isolated or trapped, being bullied or discriminated against, serious physical illness, trauma in the brain, a history of child abuse or neglect. Also, one needs to consider the social and cultural factors in which the individual is living, does the young person have a stable home? Finally, the relationship with significant others needs to be considered alongside all the other aspects I have described. For example, does the young person feel that he or she can talk to parents about feeling suicidal? The main thing to remember is suicidal thinking can occur when a person feels that they are no longer able to cope with an overwhelming situation. Many people keep their thoughts and feelings a secret, which means that parents do not always realise that there is anything wrong. I have listed in the guide for parents towards the end of this chapter warning signs that you need to look out for.

The Influence of Forums and Internet Sites on Suicide

Daine (2013) and her colleagues also carried out a systematic review into the influence of forums and general internet sites on suicidal ideation. Concerns have been raised that both offer encouragement to vulnerable adolescents to follow through on their suicidal thoughts.

Forums

Some participants in one study described forums as a way of receiving support (Collings et al., 2011). However, in another study an increase in suicidal thinking was reported by users after they had accessed forums (Dunlop et al., 2011). In a third study 14.5 per cent of users reported their involvement in accessing forums was for destructive reasons and finding a suicidal partner was relevant to 18 per cent of them (Hinduja & Patchin, 2010). There were also conflicting views in a fourth study which showed lower levels of distress in some participants, while others showed signs of worsening distress (Barak & Dolev-Cohen, 2006).

Internet sites

Fifty-nine per cent of participants in one study reported they had learnt about suicide from internet sites (Dunlop et al., 2011). In another study suicidal thinking was significantly connected with searching online for information about suicide (Katsumata et al., 2008). Online gaming exceeding five hours a day was associated with suicidal thinking and planning in a third study (Messias et al., 2011). Increased levels of internet addiction were related to increased depression and suicidal thoughts (Kim et al., 2006) and cyberbullying also increased rates of attempted suicide for both victims and perpetrators (Hinduja & Patchin, 2010).

Adam's research into the influence of forums and internet sites on suicide

I wanted to see for myself what forums and internet sites reported so I Googled 'the best way to commit suicide'. I found it was extremely helpful that the first site that came up was the NHS site on suicide with all the relevant information (www.nhs.uk/conditions/suicide/). Of the nine remaining sites, the first was run by a parent who had lost a daughter to suicide; another was managed by an investigative journalist specialising in mental health who had survived her own suicide attempt; a different site claimed to be a pro-life support forum for individuals in crisis, and they did not share methods on suicide. The remaining sites offered information on what suicide consists of, while only five sites suggested that users should see a GP.

One site offered information on a suicide kit, which I believe had been extracted from a book called *The Peaceful Pill Handbook* (Nitschke & Stewart, 2016). This website described the suicide kit as consisting of a large plastic bag with a draw cord used to commit suicide through gas asphyxiation. It is part of a device which is used in conjunction with a flow of an inert gas like helium or nitrogen, which prevents the panic, sense of suffocation and struggling before unconsciousness, known as the hypercapnic alarm response caused by the presence of high carbon dioxide concentrations in the blood (Nitschke & Stewart, 2016). The site did not explain how to die or how to obtain the kit.

One of the forum sites had an ongoing conversation between users on the best way to commit suicide which I have paraphrased.

- I've heard that using a car exhaust has minimal pain.
- I don't think there's a solution to your problem that doesn't involve pain. I would go for the same option myself. There's also the razor blades to consider.
- I would consider pills, although it's difficult to get strong ones.
- You could strangle yourself.
- You could stand in front of a train.

I cannot name the above sites but their 'chats' to other people who are feeling suicidal are shocking and frankly dangerous. There is no screening process for vulnerability on these sites beyond a question at the registration stage, and this is easily manipulated and serves only to protect the site, not the users. Even if users did highlight their vulnerability and were excluded, this could potentially do greater harm by preventing them from connecting with others, if this were the only form of contact they had with other individuals. In some of the comments, a few people try to offer hope but generally most are accepting of each other's will to die. The other concern is that often discussions around suicide on these sites are controlled by those who have no experience of suicidal ideation, or mental health issues.

—

What is surprising about Daine's (2013) and my own research is the fact that young people use forums and the internet instead of chatting to their peers about their difficulties, which is contrary to the idea that peers are important. Obviously, some would prefer to talk anonymously to a stranger. This is significant, as I believe that adopting such tactics could increase the young person's isolation and possible shame and lead to further risks of self-harming behaviour and suicidal ideation depending upon the credibility of the site.

—

My first volunteer placement as a trainee counsellor was as a bereavement counsellor for Cruse Bereavement Care (www.

cruse.org.uk), a national agency designed to offer advice and support when someone dies. It was mainly the parents of young people who died by suicide that I counselled, and such a loss was devastating to their families. I came across boys and girls who were feeing suicidal through my later work with this age group as a counsellor. I found their intent to take their own lives was the result of several things, for example, having nowhere to live, isolation, financial strain, bullying, academic pressure, and drug misuse.

Fortunately, I worked with several other agencies to reduce the risks of suicide with these young people. In most cases when reflecting on their suicidal intentions, the young people said they were extremely glad to have survived a suicidal attempt, and they were happy to be alive. The main thing that inspired them to cope with their suicidal feelings was to feel hopeful (a light at the end of the tunnel). This was achieved partly by myself being empathic and my ability to 'contain' their feelings (I did not panic) throughout the stages of their counselling. I would urge readers to try and communicate openly, compassionately, and together with those you are responsible for and who are displaying suicidal behaviour.

Guides for Parents and Teachers

Parents

It is crucial for parents to display a level of empathy so that their sons and daughters feel supported throughout the overwhelming experience of feeling suicidal. Listen to them when they appear upset or withdrawn and encourage them to talk about their worries. One way to clarify the intention of risk is to ask them where on the suicidal scale from 0 (feeling a bit low) to 10 (feeling extremely suicidal) they see themselves. That should pave the way for further discussion.

I encourage parents to look up forums and internet sites for themselves and discuss with their adolescent which ones are helpful and the ones which appear dangerous, and make sure all medicines are out of sight. Listed below are some warning signs which may help you to recognise suicidal intentions in someone you are responsible for:

- Being preoccupied with dying, suicide or death.
- Having different mood shifts, either happy or sad.
- Talking about revenge, guilt, or shame.
- Changes in personality, or sleep patterns.
- Increasing the use of drugs or alcohol.
- Acquiring substances that could end their life.
- Experiencing depression, panic attacks, or displaying a heightened state of anxiety.
- Isolating themselves and saying goodbye to others as though it were the last time.
- Talking about being a burden to others or expressing a regret about ever being born.
- Expressing severe remorse and self-criticism.
- Leaving a note or posting about suicide on social media sites.
- Being associated with someone who has completed suicide.
- Having previously attempted suicide.
- Exposure to graphic accounts of suicide.

I realise that some readers may feel overwhelmed at the

different warning signs that you need to look out for. If you care for someone who is suicidal then I suggest you follow the same guidelines I have described to minimise self-harm. Try to encourage him or her when feeling suicidal to deter from thinking about the future, and just focus on what is going on in their day-to-day experience. If possible, they should get to a safe place (a friend's house or home), or to be around other people, or to call one of the helpline numbers listed shortly. I gave my suicidal clients a laminated card the size of a credit/ debit card with telephone numbers of family, friends, or agencies they can call in an emergency. This is where a mobile phone can be helpful to contain such numbers.

Suicidal thoughts are transient (they can change from day to day) so it is important that parents track their adolescent's thoughts, feelings and behaviour. As well as looking for signs to assess the risk, listed below are some pointers that can indicate someone who had suicidal tendencies has a decreased risk of acting out suicidal thoughts.

- Looking forward to future events.
- Not wanting to affect family or friends.
- Expressing a fear of dying.
- Being left disabled by an unsuccessful suicide attempt.

This is only a guide and parents should remain vigilant. Extra support can be obtained by accessing the Samaritans or by calling them free from any phone on 116 123, or by emailing jo@samaritans.org. Papyrus is the national charity dedicated to the prevention of young suicide, offering advice for those who are feeling suicidal and those who are worried about others (www.papyrus-uk.org). If you are under 35 years of age you can call the Papyrus Helpline on 0800 0684141. I advise that if you are looking after someone who displays suicidal intentions, you can refer them to your GP for an emergency appointment, or call 111 for out of hours, or go to your A&E department. If you cannot get to a hospital, call 999 for an ambulance.

If your young person is referred to a specialist service, such as CAMHS, a detailed clinical assessment will take place to establish the level of risk of suicidal intentions. The doctors will look at whether there are any underlying mental health problems, if there are any alcohol or drug misuse issues, and whether the young person is taking any prescribed medication. Depending on the level of risk, a treatment plan will be drawn up which may consist of having to talk to a counsellor using cognitive behavioural therapy (CBT). They may be referred for family therapy or be asked to join a group discussion, and the doctors may prescribe anti-depressants. I have previously explained in Chapter 3 that the use of anti-depressants may increase the risk of suicide during the first few weeks of taking them.

Teachers

I would recommend teachers read the guide that I described in the self-harm section which also contains advice on what to do when someone attempts suicide. This guide should be read in conjunction with other relevant guidelines currently in place at your school or college. It may be prudent for teachers to adopt a suicide prevention strategy as part of the bullying policies implemented in their school.

—

Young people who self-harm or are feeling suicidal often turn to forums or internet sites for support. These sites may present an extra risk because they may normalise self-harm and suicide and discourage disclosure or seeking professional help. We must remember that primarily we are talking about vulnerable adolescents who may not have the skills to discern what is good or bad advice.

However, the potential support provided by these sites should also be considered. Alleviation of loneliness and shame, and the fact of sharing with others may be factors that decrease the need to self-harm or think about committing suicide. Managed appropriately, such sites may provide a stepping-stone for vulnerable adolescents, by giving them instant access to social networks. This allows them anonymity when learning coping strategies and seeking support for self-harming behaviours and suicidal thoughts. Given that adolescents use forums and internet sites to gain information about self-harm and suicide, responsible adults need to ensure that they monitor such sites regularly to provide supportive information to our young people through ongoing discussion.

10

THE EFFECT OF VIDEO GAMES ON ADDICTION, AGGRESSION AND LEARNING

In the 1980s games were played for fun, for example, *Pac-Man* was a favourite at that time, featuring a yellow orb that raced around the screen, gobbling up pellets to avoid being caught by ghosts. During the 1990s games changed dramatically; the most popular game, *Mortal Kombat*, displayed humanoid characters engaging in battle with the sole purpose of killing their opponents. Vast technological advances since the 1990s have made video games a psychologically rewarding experience. There are a variety of platforms individuals can use to access these games such as mobile phones, PCs, and gaming consoles. Games can be played by a single player, or by multiple players playing at the same time.

Most games focus on the advancement of the user who becomes an online character called an avatar (a figure representing a particular person), in which players control their avatar's physical features, and characteristics. The avatar's achievement is advanced through his or her engagement with the mission, by fighting a fake opponent, competing with one's own skills, or to beat a high score or pre-set standard.

This often involves the user obtaining specific items along the way, and the development of multi-tasking skills, high levels of concentration, and the ability to eliminate opponents are all advantageous. The scenarios which create the adventure only exist for the duration of the game, but games can be reinstated at the original point for an unlimited number of times.

While reasons to play online games differ according to gender, age, and personality, a few common elements in the appeal of video games rank consistently high as factors. Some gamers often build relationships with other online players as an escape from reality. The online space might be the place where gamers feel they are accepted (Young, 2009), especially if they become preoccupied with gaming and lose interest in other activities.

Another appeal of gaming is that the brain releases dopamine, a pleasure chemical, during video game playing. As adolescent years are depicted by heightened social behaviour, such as attention-seeking and risk-taking, relationships take on a greater significance. Because adolescents' brains are still learning to control impulses, regulate emotions, and assess risks and consequences throughout this stage, they may be willing to take risks online (Crone & Konijn, 2018). Thus, seeking out fun and exciting experiences are a high priority on young people's lists (Steinberg, 2007) and playing video games can fall into this category.

Gender Identity

Research has supported the fact that males play video games more frequently than females (Win & Heeter, 2009; Padilla-Walker et al., 2010). One of the original reasons there was a lack of female gamers was because there was a gender bias towards male characters always playing the lead role. Gender refers to the characteristics of human beings that are partially socially constructed, and includes norms, behaviours and roles associated with being a male or female (Berkowitz et al., 2010). There are current stereotypes about what both genders represent, for example, males are traditionally thought of as being tough and muscular, whereas most individuals think girls are compassionate and have nurturing characteristics.

A report produced by researchers of Cambridge BETA (2020) explains why gender and game playing is still not balanced between the two sexes (beta.cambridgeenglish.org). When video games were first introduced it was primarily for male interest, and because of this they were marketed towards the male population. When more females started taking an interest in gaming, many males felt that their hobby was being encroached upon by females which led to their community being hostile towards females (beta.cambridgeenglish.org). This is another of the early factors that deterred females from playing games (beta.cambridgeenglish.org).

In the past there have been three identities for females in video games. One is the helpless victim, i.e. Princess Peach in *Mario* or Princess Zelda in *The Legend of Zelda* where both females are locked up and a male hero rescues them. Another is a female character portrayed as a mighty warrior, who is shown as semi-naked, or not wearing acceptable clothing for her to face her dangerous task. One example is Lara Croft from the original *Tomb Raider*.

Another description of females in early video games can be known as 'the pink one' (beta.cambridgeenglish.org). These characters are different to other characters in the game, but they are recognised as female because they are wearing pink or have long eyelashes or a bow. So, anyone playing these types of games would discover that the female protagonist is either a victim, a sex object or 'the pink one' (beta.cambridgeenglish. org).

Things have improved as far as the portrayals of females in games is concerned. Some games have one main protagonist, who is female, for instance, Lara Croft in the rebooted *Tomb Raider* is now dressed as if she is ready for the assignment which she is going to face. The researchers found when they trialled a game called *Ruby Rei*, a female space explorer, fifteen boys volunteered but only three girls came forward. The researchers thought the girls were not as interested as the boys because they lacked familiarity with gaming and feared showing themselves as incompetent, or, due to social pressures, they wanted to be perceived as feminine. For some females, video games are not seen as feminine, and to maintain their social status they chose to reject the opportunity to play video games (beta. cambridgeenglish.org). The researchers concluded that game developers should consider how characters are described and that characters should be portrayed as human beings and not through the lens of stereotypical myths to make the gender balance equal (beta.cambridgeenglish.org). I acknowledge that some companies are now successfully achieving that.

Addiction

In their review into video gaming addiction, Kuss and Griffiths (2012) report that multi-player games are the most addictive of all because of the possibility of creating new worlds. This enhances the gamers' social environment and increases the potential for gamers to become attached and identify with their avatar. Previous research shows that participants' life satisfaction influenced the personalities and identification of their avatars (Trepte & Reinecke, 2010). When individuals are satisfied with their lives, they create avatars that resemble themselves, but those who felt dissatisfied constructed avatars that are different to them (Trepte & Reinecke, 2010). I believe some gamers, i.e. those who are feeling isolated, become emotionally dependent on their avatars, and are as attached to them as someone in the real world may be attached to a real relationship.

Another study into video game addiction, led by Sarah Coyne, investigated adolescents as they progressed from childhood into adulthood (www.sciencedaily). All the participants completed questionnaires once a year over a six-year period which measured depression, anxiety, aggression, delinquency, empathy, anti-social behaviour, shyness, sensory reactivity, financial stress, and problematic mobile phone use (www.sciencedaily). The results showed that 90 per cent of this group did not suffer from harmful or negative long-term consequences. However, the remaining 10 per cent of participants fell into the pathological (those who behave in an extreme way) video gameplay category, and as a result suffered mental health problems both socially and in their behaviour. When compared to the non-pathological group (those who behave normally) these participants displayed higher levels of depression, aggression, shyness, problematic mobile phone use and anxiety by the time they had developed into adulthood. All participants had the same measures at the same time which suggests that video games may have played a role in developing these negative outcomes (www. sciencedaily).

The amount of time that video games get played is frequently discussed in households where young people live. In today's world where young people are growing up with digital technology parents can play a critical role in helping them to learn healthy ways of gaming. A recent survey undertaken by C.S. Mott Children's Hospital (mottpoll.org) report that parents of adolescents aged under 18 years believe gaming has the potential to have both a positive and negative impact on their adolescents. But most parents in this study have concerns regarding the amount of time their adolescents spend gaming.

There was a noticeable difference between the two genders, with twice as many parents describing that their boys play video games every day (41 per cent), compared to parents of girls (20 per cent). When they play video games, the boys are more likely than girls to spend 3 or more hours gaming (37 per cent vs. 19 per cent). Among the parents who claim their adolescents play games every day, 54 per cent reported continued gaming of three hours or more (mottpoll.org). Overall, the parents report that by playing games excessively this impacted negatively upon their adolescents' family activities, sleep habits, homework, and friendships with peers who do not play games (mottpoll.org).

Video gaming is becoming extremely addictive because it is designed to be that way. Video game designers are trying to make a profit and are always looking for ways to get more people playing their games. The designers achieve this by making a game just challenging enough to keep the user coming back for more, but not so hard that the user gives up. These games are planned to draw the user in, to guarantee that each level is rewarded by the next level. If individuals take a break, they either suffer in the game or they feel disheartened due to the lack of rewarding game play. An important feature that keeps gamers playing is the anticipation that another 'reward' is just over the horizon.

It is impossible to predict with any accuracy whether your sons or daughters will become addicted to video game playing. But, for some young people, their lives have shifted online into an unreal world, and this may result in a fragmented set of experiences that carry no weight in the real world. For example, they might start to feel uncertain about who they are. So, they turn to video gaming because it is an artificial world where they feel good about themselves as they are having fun, and they are shutting out the kinds of experiences that would make them feel unhappy or anxious (Ferguson & Olson, 2013). Moderation and common sense play an important role in managing video gaming, but problems arise when hours of playing time start to encroach on other activities, including schoolwork, family life and seeing friends. As parents you can exert some control if your adolescents' gaming habits start affecting their lives, or if you notice a change in their emotional state or behaviour.

Emotional signs

Emotional signs of addiction could include:

- Feelings of restlessness and/or irritability when unable to play games.
- Constantly talking about previous games or anticipating the next game.
- Lying about the amount of time spent playing.
- Becoming isolated from friends or family to spend more time gaming.

- Symptoms of depression or anxiety, which were not there previously.

Physical signs

Physical signs of addiction include the following:

- Tiredness or fatigue, particularly after playing games late into the night.
- Frequent headaches/migraines due to periods of intense concentration.
- Neglecting personal hygiene.
- Carpal tunnel syndrome caused by the overuse of a controller.

Though most of the symptoms listed above have short-term effects, they can have more severe long-term repercussions if not addressed properly. Someone addicted to video games will often avoid sleeping or eating proper meals to continue gaming. While the short-term effects of this may include hunger and fatigue, it could eventually lead to a sleep disorder or diet-related health issues. Similarly, those who isolate themselves from others to play video games may miss out on family events, or outings with friends. If this continues for a long period of time, gamers may find themselves without any friends at all.

Guides for Parents

Gaming addiction is categorised as an impulse control disorder, which means that individuals in this category may struggle to manage their urges to play video games and can experience withdrawal symptoms should they not be able to continue game playing. Parents should be watchful for signs that gaming is becoming a compulsion for their adolescents. There are several self-help strategies which work towards a reduction in the amount of time that young people spend playing games. The following advice is focused on moderating behaviours and creating a level of emotional control which means that you can limit their gaming time to an acceptable amount.

Check the age guidelines of the video games

It is hard to stick to the ratings especially when all their friends are playing the same game. But common sense should prevail.

Some games are designed to be more addictive than others

Any pressure in a game is specifically programmed to be addictive and that is where the problems begin. For example, games where adolescents are part of a community or where they will be letting other players down if they do not participate is a particular concern. Where possible choose games that can be played in short bursts of time.

Discuss the reasons why you are setting gaming restrictions

Explain that playing games is a form of entertainment and that success in the gaming world is imaginary and not what their real lives are about. It has nothing to do with real life success where it is more worthwhile to earn points by getting good grades, earning real money, or learning a useful skill which will be beneficial in later life.

Limit screen time

Jenny Radesky, a developmental behavioural paediatrician and researcher at Mott Children's Hospital, claims that the American Academy of Paediatrics (APA) recommends that young people should be allowed no more than two hours a day of video game playing (health blog.uofmhealth.org). Unfortunately, this advice is not broken down into age range. However, she does suggest that parents create a timetable where young people can play their games without affecting their homework and behaviour.

Track your adolescent's game time

The popular games are designed to be deeply engaging, and young people can easily lose track of time playing them. Most games entice adolescents to keep moving up levels, or to keep trying until they succeed. Logging a young person's game time can make them aware of how much of their time is spent playing games. If they play games excessively, it can be a wake-up call for you to ensure they cut back on that time.

Inappropriate games

No matter what restrictions you place on your sons and daughters' game playing eventually they will be exposed to other material that concerns you such as violence or sex. Young people need to know how to handle or ignore such content when you are not around.

Play games with your adolescents

I have played the game *Fortnite* with my two 12-year-old grandsons Freddy and Riley, along with an 8-year-old Oscar who manages to keep up with the older two. I realised that some of the attraction was that they could be connected to their friends. Other reasons are they like collecting characters in the same way they would collect small toys or cards when they were younger, and by completing levels this gives them greater access to collecting special characters. I have also noticed that when Freddy and Oscar play as a team, they organise themselves into roles and have good communication to win. That would not normally happen because of the age gap in other pursuits, in which they may argue with each other.

Check who plays with your adolescents

When I observed Freddy and Riley playing with a stranger on their headsets, they told me that some people swear at them and call them 'rubbish'. Apart from the bad language, comments like these can make young people lose their confidence. Also, I would encourage you to check who your sons and daughters are playing with for safety reasons.

Encourage your adolescents to participate in other activities

Try to get them to participate in alternative activities. These can range from physical events like playing sports, running, learning to play an instrument, or joining a dance group. Some young people may enjoy joining a youth organisation to make new friends, to learn skills that will be useful later in life. For example, they can increase their communication and decision-making skills, through volunteering or participating in community projects, which may lead to increased self-confidence.

Professional advice

If you are worried about your adolescent's gaming habit, I would suggest you get help by contacting your GP. Gaming addiction is now recognised as a mental health condition by the World Health Organisation (www.who.int). WHO describes the condition as being characterised by a pattern of recurrent, digital-gaming or video-gaming behaviour. Individuals who have this disorder will have difficulty controlling their gaming habits and this results in gaming taking precedence over other interests and daily activities. They state that for a diagnosis for gaming addiction, the behaviour of the individual must be severe enough to result in a deterioration in personal, family, social, educational, occupational, or other important areas of functioning. They will normally diagnose an addiction if any of these factors have been evident for at least twelve months. However, they add that this duration may be shortened if all diagnostic requirements are met, and symptoms are severe (www.who.int).

Young people aged between thirteen and twenty-five who have a gaming addiction will be offered treatment on the NHS. Healthcare professionals will accept referrals from the NHS-funded Centre for Internet and Gaming Disorders. They will provide treatment over Skype as part of their service. Simon Stevens, chief executive of the NHS, explained that the new service is a response to an emerging problem, part of the increasing pressures that children and young people are exposed to these days. "Concerns surrounding the length of time children and adolescents are spending online playing games are growing, specifically the effect it can have on a young person's mental health" (www.england.nhs.uk). Video games are a part of our world today. However, time spent gaming should not be at the expense of face-to-face time with family, friends, and teachers who play a pivotal and important role in promoting adolescents' learning and healthy development.

Aggression

The relationship between violent video games and adolescent aggression has become a hot topic in research studies (Anderson et al., 2010; Ferguson et al., 2012; Greitemeyer, 2014).

General Aggressive Model

The General Aggressive Model (GAM) provides a comprehensive framework and is best known by research undertaken by Craig Anderson who has carried out influential investigations into the effect of violent video games for children and adolescents. He suggested that based on this model the degree of exposure to violent video games leads to an increase of aggression and is influenced by previous knowledge of social learning theory. Social learning theory developed by Bandura (1977) emphasises the importance of observing and modelling the behaviours, attitudes, and emotional reactions of others. In his experiment of aggression by using a large inflatable doll known as the 'Bobo Doll', a team of researchers physically and verbally abused this doll in front of a group of pre-school children. This led to the same children mimicking the behaviour of the adults

Figure 10.0 A Child Attacking the Bobo Doll.
Illustration by Barbara Lambert.

by attacking the doll in a similar fashion. Bandura (1977) claimed his experiment showed that violent behaviour which is affected by aggressive thoughts and feelings results from the development, and reinforcement, of aggression that individuals have seen or heard in other aggression-related contexts.

The GAM model was used by Anderson and Dill (2000) to determine the effects of violence from video games played by adolescent students, where they focused on the potentially negative consequences of long-term exposure to video games. The researchers measured the amount of exposure by asking the participants their favourite games, and the amount of time they had played these games irrespective of their content. They also asked them to fill in questionnaires to assess whether watching violent video games could act as a predictor of aggressive behaviour or aggressive delinquency by asking the following questions: "How many times in the past year have you threatened to hit someone?" and for non-aggressive delinquency, "How many times have you purposely destroyed property belonging to your parents?" (Anderson & Dill 2000). The study found that students who reported playing more violent video games over a period of years also engaged in more aggressive behaviour in their own lives. This was linked primarily to aggressive delinquent behaviour. This relation was stronger for students who have aggressive personalities and for men (Anderson & Dill 2000).

The Catalyst Model

Ferguson et al., (2008) proposed, according to the Catalyst Model (CM), violent behaviour is the cause of a mixture of genetic characteristics as well as influences by the family environment. That is, an individual's genes can directly lead to aggressive child temperaments and aggressive adult personalities. Individuals who have aggressive temperaments or aggressive personalities are more likely to produce violent behaviour during times of environmental strain. Violence is also influenced indirectly by the family and exposure to media or peer violence (Ferguson et al., 2008).

The GAM vs. the CM

In a more recent study Shao and Wang (2019) investigated aggressive outcomes from playing video games when they compared the GAM to the CM. The researchers used self-report questionnaires to collect data on adolescents' exposure to violent video games, their family environment along with their normative beliefs about aggression. Normative beliefs refer to an individual's degree of acceptance of aggression which affects their choice of behaviour. The researchers combined the participants' normative beliefs along with analysing their family environments, which consisted of either good support from family members, containing an emphasis on ethics, religion, and values, or to a less supportive family where there was anger from family members and less emphasis on ethics, religion, and values.

Moderated mediation model

To analyse their findings, the researchers constructed a new moderated mediation model (MM) model which included aspects of both the GAM and the CM. Their results showed a significant link between exposure to violent video games and adolescent aggression (GAM). Shao and Wang's (2019) results also found firstly that those adolescents who had high scores on the family environment (CM) often help each other, seldom show angry feelings, and are more attentive to morality and values. These positive aspects will assist adolescents to understand violence in video games from the right perspective and lessen the effect of violent video games on normative beliefs about aggression.

On the other hand, adolescents with low scores of family environment are less likely to help each other, frequently show anger, and pay less attention to morality and values. These negative aspects increase their acceptance of violence and aggression, and because of the lack of family structure, exposure to violent video games could significantly predict normative beliefs about aggression.

Summary

Shao and Wang (2019) claimed the MM model recognised greater insights into the effect of violent video games on aggression. For example, by encouraging adolescents to distinguish between violence in games and reality, the role of normative beliefs about aggression could help them to identify rational ways to resolve aggressive tendencies without hurtful consequences. The researchers suggested that more attention should be paid to the important role of the family environment as this is closely related to adolescent aggression. Parents should try to create a good family atmosphere, showing anger and aggression as little as possible, and practise positive moral values (Shao & Wang, 2019). By exhibiting this behaviour parents can minimise the negative effect of exposure to violent video games.

Guides for Parents and Teachers

Parents

It can be challenging for parents to provide all the ingredients such as a stable home, and to encourage friendships with others who are not aggressive, particularly as violent video games are becoming more graphic, more violent, and more realistic in their content. For those adolescents who are already displaying aggressive behaviour, I fear by playing games excessively they could increase their aggressive thoughts and feelings even further.

One of the main triggers for aggression is a feeling of frustration or anger. My experience of counselling angry young people has mainly resulted in their anger relating to a lot of earlier issues which have accumulated over time. They then get angry with someone in the present and direct all their anger onto that person. It is important that parents try to understand the difference between the root cause of their son's or daughter's anger, and to check if it is the same as angry feelings they are experiencing in the moment.

A good way to detect whether your adolescent's anger is related to the here-and-now, or whether it is a long-standing issue is to notice whether they show excessive anger over something that appears insignificant. Ask them how long they have experienced their anger, and do they know what it is related to. There are times when situations may warrant a strong reaction, for example, they had to rush to get the school bus. But if your adolescent loses their temper towards you for forgetting to wake them up (instead of him or her using an alarm), it is quite likely the anger that they feel may have already been there, just waiting for an opportunity to erupt.

Common roots of anger include fear, frustration, anxiety, shame, sadness, guilt, disappointment, embarrassment, and jealousy. Helping young people to address their anger as it arises should stop a strong emotion from being buried and building up again. The more your young person can make the connection between what leads to his or her angry outbursts, the more control they will have in expressing this emotion. Once you have both established the reason of their anger then encourage them to use one of the strategies listed below to try to manage it.

Participate in physical activities

The impulse to do something physical when feeling angry is strong in most adolescents. Involvement in sports on a regular basis helps with expressing anger.

Hit a punch bag

Young people need safe ways to get their anger out; a punch bag works well, as does hitting a pillow.

Take time out

When anger escalates adolescents may need time alone to calm down and yell, cry or whatever is needed so they stay safe and do not hurt others.

Use music

Music works well to help adolescents to identify and express feelings of anger, whether through singing, dancing, or playing along with songs filled with rage.

When your son or daughter has calmed down and you are discussing strategies to help with their anger ask them what they could do differently to solve the problem. For those parents who feel their adolescent's aggressive behaviour seems difficult to control, then I suggest you take them to your GP, who may be able to help by referring them for counselling or family therapy. Sometimes it is necessary for counsellors to consider other members of the family to see if anyone else is influencing a young person's angry behaviour.

Teachers

Teachers should follow their school's Behaviour Policy which is required by law under the advice of the government's Department of Education guidance. This guide includes what constitutes inappropriate behaviour and gives clear guidance, including relevant sanctions on how to deal with these types of behaviour for head teachers and school staff. For further information please access the following website: www.gov.uk/government/publications/behaviour-and-discipline-in-schools.

—

Although this section of the chapter has focused on the potential violence that playing video games can bring, I wish to acknowledge that there are many games for adolescent boys and girls which include non-violent content and encourage creative thinking.

Learning

There has been a greater reliance on technology in schools not only for teacher-parent communication, but technology has also become embedded within school projects and homework.

There are some advantages of video games which have been designed for learning particularly during the coronavirus pandemic of 2020. While, in the past, games have been used to support professional development and training requirements, today this approach is being adopted in schools and colleges. Universities are now using this form of learning, especially in business training, for many students.

The traditional approach of teachers 'talking at' pupils from the front of the classroom has now changed. It has been replaced with a different role of facilitating adolescents' education by providing opportunities for active learning. By using a practical hands-on experience, adolescents will become more active in their own learning, solving problems, developing communication skills which can lead to shared thinking and greater knowledge.

Immersive learning (deeply engaging) is the process of learning by using an artificial environment and enables adolescents to become engaged in learning that feels as close as possible to experiencing the 'real' thing (de Freitas, 2006). For example, if adolescents are studying WWII then the learning environment could reflect elements of the war such as videos showing combat in action, and the armoury which was used during that time, along with first-hand accounts of soldiers who returned home. This type of learning 'in action' encourages pupils to be engaged.

Parents and teachers should be checking not only the outcome but the process of their adolescent's learning by reflecting on their displays. Examples of photographs, videos, and handwritten stories can be used to record their learning journeys (de Freitas, 2006). Regardless of the method, adolescents should be part of the process and be encouraged to share their work with their peers, family members and teaching staff throughout the academic year. This reflective cycle capitalises on adolescents' ideas and interests and puts learning into context through an immersive space. With teachers' support this can help them to achieve a deeper understanding of the learning process by themselves (de Freitas, 2006).

Motivation is a key aspect of effective learning, but it needs to be maintained through feedback responses, reflection, and active involvement for learning to take place (Garris et al., 2002). Factors which have implications upon player's motivation to play games have been identified as, a sense of challenge, that games are realistic, opportunities to discover new information and to have learner control (Garris et al., 2002). Therefore, a significant challenge for effective learning with games is for the learner to be engaged, motivated, supported and interested but also for the learning to be undertaken in relation to clear learning outcomes as well as being made relevant to real-world contexts of practice (de Freitas, 2006).

I realise it is extremely difficult for parents to get their adolescents motivated to work online while the schools are shut during this latest period of lockdown (January 2021). I have first-hand experience of coaching my two twelve-year-old grandsons while both daughters go to work. I have found it is harder for them to become motivated because some of the classes are not live lessons. There are many websites which suggest ways of teaching your child or adolescent online and I have listed some of the best suggestions below.

Guides for Parents and Teachers

Parents

Create a stress-free environment

If a young person is stressed this will inhibit the pre-frontal cortex from functioning and they will not be able to think effectively. Manage your own stress levels by going for a walk or doing an activity and encourage your sons or daughters to join you.

Provide structure and routine

Make sure they have their laptops ready to start a lesson on time.

Focus on learning and not their performance

If your young person is struggling to get all their class subjects in on time focus on the learning aspect of the class. What did he or she learn, and be enthusiastic about what their strengths are.

Encourage learning on a day-to-day basis

Sometimes there are opportunities to help your adolescents to think critically in normal life. For example, I recently had a conversation with Riley about the value of going for a walk while exercising my dog, i.e. you can keep fit by walking. By changing every day into a learning experience, it will help your adolescents to develop the motivation to learn in the classroom, at home or wherever they may be.

Teachers

I would encourage teachers to read online a report by De Freitas (2006) called *Learning in immersive worlds: a review of game-*

based learning. There is a wealth of information that teachers can use; particularly as some of you will be attempting to teach your pupils distance learning while the schools are closed.

11

The review of literature featured in this book alongside my own research identifies there is a distinct difference for the mental health and well-being of today's adolescents i.e. the Digital Natives compared to individuals that Prensky (2000) calls the Digital Immigrants. The evidence presented suggests that it appears a lot harder for our young people today to adjust from being a child into adulthood as they attempt to develop their identities and personalities using digital technology as part of their daily lives. I believe it is a combination of several factors, which I will summarise shortly. But primarily it is because adolescents must navigate through this digital world to try and be themselves, be part of a peer group, have meaningful relationships, and fit into society.

Social Media: Benefits and Risks

Benefits

As digital forms of communication become normal for young people, it is not surprising that they choose to convey personal information by using their mobile phones, social media platforms and websites. The ever-expanding display of social media applications that are continually introduced into young people's culture are creating new virtual spaces and communities. This provides adolescents with affirming environments where they can explore their identities and personalities and connect with like-minded others. The sense of control and independence by using digital technology, is significant for adolescents as gaining autonomy from parents is an important milestone in their identity development (Noom, Dekovic, & Meeus, 2001).

In creating a coherent sense of self, adolescents are more likely to pass successfully through the stages of identity development (Erikson, 1995) and live meaningful lives. A research review by Nezlek, Hampton, and Shean (2000) concluded that those who experience greater intimacy and meaningful relationships will also develop a stronger well-being. Additionally, the anonymity of social media can promote the help-seeking process by lowering the barriers of self-disclosure which means individuals can access support without anyone knowing who they are. This was particularly relevant during the discussion in the suicide section.

Risks

The importance of social media is further emphasised when one considers the psychological costs associated with the suppression of emotions caused by limited social support. However, accessing social media sites for support such as getting advice on eating disorders, sexuality orientation, self-harm, and suicide needs to be done with care. Many websites are not run by professionals and carry the wrong type of advice which may impound the user's mental health difficulties. Also, young people should be warned about the potential dangers of engaging in identity exploration in public virtual spaces, as they are often not focused on future consequences and may not think about the long-term effects of posting confidential personal information online. For example, the literature shows that cyberbullying, being stigmatised for being part of an LGBT group, and online racism all carry greater mental health risks such as depression, anxiety, self-harm, and suicidal thinking than traditional offline discrimination. Online safety is a major concern for adolescents, as some of them may not be aware of the way in which perpetrators groom their victims with a view to exposing them to dangerous offline meetings.

When adolescents share their thoughts, feelings, and experiences with a larger audience online this can contribute to the creation of social norms leading to the pressure to 'fit in' amongst their peer group. If they do not feel they can be part of their group, this may lead to a lack of confidence and promote feelings of low self-esteem. It seems many young people want to look the same and behave in the same way as their peers and this can eliminate any sense of self. This was the case with the young women who were described in the body image chapter.

The literature shows that girls are having a more difficult time than boys to manage their online self-presentation, their developing identities, and personalities effectively. It is made more difficult for the girls as one of the leading social media sites, i.e. Facebook use the concept of 'likes' as an indication of a person's status and popularity (Oberst et al., 2016). Girls are more susceptible to their online images being perceived as perfect as they are more persuaded than the boys to copy models and famous celebrities. Research also shows girls are more likely to develop eating disorders and have an increased rate of self-harm and suicidal behaviour if they do not receive a high number of 'likes' for the images they post (Chua & Chang, 2016).

Advice for Parents and Teachers

Parents

Developing an acceptable way to talk to your adolescents about accessing social media is crucial. However, you may feel that you do not understand the latest technology, apps or social media that your adolescent is using, but do not let that put you off. Ask your son or daughter to teach you and show you their favourite apps, games, or websites. This will help you to appreciate why they use these sites and how they work so that you can talk about the positives and whether you have any concerns.

Depending upon the age of your adolescent, if you discover they are accessing inappropriate content (violence, sexual content, nasty comments), tell them that you will not overreact if they tell you about something disturbing they have seen. Wherever possible, make it a joint decision so they understand the reasons not to access these sites and persuade them to stick to your wishes. If necessary, help them to report or block content they find disturbing. It is important to make sure they can make good decisions for themselves and you should try and teach them how to assess the risks and stay safe more independently as they grow older.

Teachers

The fact that young people access social media for health-related issues such as self-harm and suicide offers a potentially fruitful area for the application of some of these websites to help improve the lives of our young people. For example, teachers in schools could listen to young people's views on mental health issues and seize this opportunity to reach out with accurate information and support. Building adolescents' mental health into the school curriculum may offset some of the dangers that social media bring.

Both Parents and Teachers

Social media can offer powerful insights into the lives of young people today. Parents and teachers need to learn how to recognise and understand the virtual landscape where our young people reside for much of their daily lives. I suggest that both should acquaint themselves with the social media networking sites that their adolescents use, paying particular attention to the privacy laws. This is to ensure they understand these privacy settings as they vary with different social media sites and information that is viewed publicly can change over time. I would encourage you to ensure the validity and reliability of the information available and improve adolescents' knowledge and awareness of the high-risk situations that come along with accessing social media.

For readers who have access to Netflix, I recommend you watch *Social Dilemma*, a documentary-drama that explores the dangerous human impact of social networking. It also shows some of the tech experts who generated these sites sounding the alarm on their own creations and not letting their children have access to them. Other founders of these sites put boundaries in place to ensure the safety of their children and adolescents. The main purpose of these sites is also being targeted by multimillion-pound corporations whose sole purpose is to collect personal data to influence buying habits.

Becoming a Digital Native

During my research into social media, I already had a Facebook author's page, a Twitter account, and LinkedIn account to market my first book. Thinking about how the number of 'likes' are so important to many young people reminded me of the time when my Facebook author's page was set up. Initially I got messages from Facebook saying, "Steph Adam has not received any likes this week". This information was sent to try to encourage me to use Facebook more frequently. I found these comments extremely irritating, and for others who are more sensitive than myself, trying to promote their books and business, it could be a blow for them to receive such comments. Fortunately, Facebook was only one of the marketing tools I used to promote my first book. So, the moral of this story is, to encourage your adolescents to do other things so that they may be appreciated by others, rather than relying on social media to collect a high number of 'likes'. During the Covid pandemic, I have learnt how to use Zoom for my dance and recreational classes, use the internet much more to shop online, and have discarded my pay and go phone for a swish new contract one. All with a view to becoming a veteran Digital Native.

—

Today's young people approach their lives in different ways by communicating online which can feel alien to us Digital Immigrants. Nevertheless, they are human beings and have thoughts and feelings which influence their behaviour in the same way as older generations. The big difference is adolescents are more exposed to harmful experiences from the influence of social media, as well as gaining beneficial knowledge from going on these sites.

During this year we have all had to learn how to communicate differently with each other, and I am always being told to "keep safe", to prevent catching Covid. We all know that this pandemic is an invisible killer to our global society. I think we should pass this message on to all adolescents by trying to teach them to be safe from the invisible influences that social media can bring, by reinforcing the benefits and risks. If we all play a part, we can carry forward an investment for future generations to come.

APPENDIX A

ERIKSON'S STAGES OF IDENTITY DEVELOPMENT

Stage 1: Infant–18 months. Trust vs. Mistrust

During this stage infants are dependent upon their parents (as well as adult caregivers) for everything to survive including, food, warmth, safety, and nurturing. If infants receive these fundamental needs, they will develop trust and feel safe and secure in their world. If parents fail to provide adequate care and love, the infants will feel that they cannot trust the adults in their life and they will see their world as unpredictable. Erikson (1995) believed that successful development in this stage is about striking a balance between the two opposing sides. When this happens, infants acquire 'hope', which is an openness to experience tempered by a wariness that danger may also exist.

Stage 2: 18 months–3 years. Autonomy vs. Shame and Doubt

This stage takes place during early childhood and is focused on children developing a greater sense of personal control and learning how to gain a little independence. By allowing children to make choices and gain control, caregivers can help them to develop a sense of autonomy (independence) for example, in potty training. Erikson (1995) thought that learning to control one's bodily functions leads to a sense of independence. If children are not given the opportunity to assert themselves, they begin to feel inadequate, may become dependent upon others, and feel a sense of shame or doubt in their abilities. Achieving a balance between autonomy and shame and doubt will lead to the quality of 'will', that is, the belief that children can act with intention, within reason and limits.

Stage 3: 3–5 years. Initative vs. Guilt

During preschool years and as part of their development, children begin to declare their control over the world through directing play and other social interactions. Children who can explore their environment, show initiative, and are capable of leading others will be successful in this stage. Those children who are stifled by parents to develop such skills will experience feelings of guilt which will inhibit their creativity. This results in a lack of initiative to do anything else. When an ideal balance of individual initiative and a willingness to work with others is achieved, the quality known as 'purpose' emerges.

Stage 4: 5–12 years. Industry vs. Inferiority

Children need to cope with new social and academic demands during this stage. Through social interactions, children begin to develop a sense of pride in their accomplishments and through achieving their goals they will feel industrious. Those children who receive little encouragement from parents, or teachers, will doubt their abilities to be successful and this may lead to inferiority complexes. Successfully finding a balance at this stage of development leads to the strength known as 'competence', in which children develop a belief in their abilities to handle the tasks set before them.

Stage 5: 12-18 years. Identity vs. Confusion

This stage takes place during the turbulent adolescent years and plays a significant role in developing a sense of personal identity which will continue to influence behaviour and development for the rest of the individual's life. Adolescents need to explore different aspects of their selves and those who receive proper encouragement and reinforcement through personal exploration will emerge from this stage with a strong sense of self and feelings of independence and control. Adolescents who remain unsure of their beliefs and desires will feel insecure and confused about themselves and the future. Those who conform to parents' wishes develop weak selves, leading to role confusion. Those who are successful develop 'fidelity', which is regarded as evidence that they have successfully negotiated this transitional stage and experienced a positive resolution to the identity crisis.

Stage 6: 18–40 years. Intimacy vs. Isolation

This phase of early adulthood is when young adults need to form intimate, loving relationships with other people.

Erikson (1995) believed it was vital that people develop close, committed relationships with other people. Avoiding intimate relationships results in a failure in this stage and leads to loneliness and isolation. Successful resolution of this stage results in the quality known as 'love', which is marked by the ability to form lasting, meaningful relationships with other people.

Stage 7: 40–65 years. Generativity vs. Stagnation

Adults need to create or nurture things that will outlast them, often by having children or creating a positive change that benefits other people. This is called generativity which means leaving a mark on society that will outlive the person. Being proud of your accomplishments, watching your children grow into adults, and developing a sense of unity with your life partner are important accomplishments of this stage. Those who are successful during this phase will feel that they are contributing to the world by being active in their home and community. 'Care' is the quality achieved when this stage is handled successfully. By failing to contribute to society people feel stagnant and unproductive which results in a shallow involvement in the world.

Stage 8: 65 years to the end of life. Integrity vs. Despair

Individuals in late adulthood who reflect on their lives and are proud of their accomplishments feel a sense of integrity and they look back on their lives with few regrets. Success in this stage results in the virtue of 'wisdom' which gives individuals a sense of closure and an ability to accept death without fear. Others who are not successful may feel their lives have been wasted and face the end of their lives with feelings of bitterness and despair.

APPENDIX B

BULLYING: TEMPLATE LETTERS

Letters to school

Class teacher or head of year

Dear Miss Metcalfe   8 November 2020

I am writing to inform you that my son Jimmy Holmes has been bullied on the way home from school by Harry Waters. I would appreciate an appointment to discuss this with you as soon as possible with a view to stopping the bullying. Can you please also provide me with your anti-bullying policy before our meeting. Thank you.

Head teacher

If the situation continues then send a second letter to the head teacher.

Dear Mr West   22 November 2020

I have written letters to Miss Metcalfe concerning the bullying of my son Jimmy Holmes. Despite meeting with Miss Metcalfe, the bullying is still going on. Jimmy is becoming increasingly withdrawn and frightened, and I am extremely concerned for his well-being. I would like to arrange a meeting with yourself and Miss Metcalfe as a matter of urgency. On the day of the meeting, I would like to see a copy of Jimmy's school records to see what has been recorded. I would then like to discuss and put in place an action plan to ensure that the situation is going to be monitored towards an appropriate resolution.

Can you also confirm whether you will be involving the family of Harry Waters, the boy who is bullying Jimmy? Would it be possible for you to increase supervision at the time most of the bullying happens, at break time, in the corridors, in the changing room, and at lunchtime? Please put a copy of this complaint into Jimmy's file together with your written response. Thank you.

Board of Governors

If the bullying continues then write a letter to the Chair of the Board of Governors. You can get their name from the school office and send the letter to the school address.

Dear Mr Johnson   6 December 2020

I met with Miss Metcalfe and Mr West on 1 December 2020 to discuss the bullying of my son Jimmy Holmes who is attending Bradfield Secondary School. I enclose copies of all correspondence with the school as well as a copy of Jimmy's bullying diary which he has completed after each incident along with the effect the bullying is having on his mental health.

It has now reached the point where I feel that I am putting Jimmy in danger by sending him to school which is a matter of grave concern in terms of safeguarding. I do not feel that the school is following the guidelines laid out in its anti-bullying policy and I therefore write to you to request your intervention in this matter to ensure that this bullying is stopped as soon as possible. If I do not hear back from you within two weeks, I will write to the Local Education Authority.

Letters to other agencies

Local Education Authority

Dear Sir/Madam   22 December 2020

I am the parent of Jimmy Holmes who is in year 8 at Bradfield Secondary School and he has been experiencing bullying since 8 November 2020. I first wrote to the school on that day and have had several meetings as well as writing to the head teacher and the Board of Governors. I enclose copies of all correspondence as well as copies of the bullying diaries which my son has been completing after each bullying incident.

I have asked the school on several occasions to resolve this situation but to date have not received a satisfactory conclusion to the matter. I am therefore writing to you to request that a formal investigation is put in place in relation to my complaint. I would like a full written response following your investigation, detailing your findings. I would be grateful if you could give this matter your immediate attention to ensure Jimmy's safety at school.

Ombudsman/MP/ Secretary of State

If you have not received a satisfactory response from the

Local Education Authority (LEA) you can write to the Local Government Ombudsman. Details of how to complain are on their website: www.lgo.org.uk/make-a-complaint.

You can also contact your local Member of Parliament (MP) and ask for their intervention to try and achieve a resolution. You can find out who your local MP is by searching with your postcode on the following website: www.parliament.uk/mps-lords-and-offices/mps/.

The final option is to write to, The Secretary of State, Sanctuary Buildings, Great Smith Street, Westminster, London, SW1P 3BT.

REFERENCES

Abrutyn, S. and Mueller, A. S. (2014) Are suicidal behaviours contagious in adolescence? Using longitudinal data to examine suicide suggestion. *American Sociological Review,* [Accessed 22 June 2019] https://doi. org/10.1177/0003122413519445.

Advertising Standards Authority, (ASA) (2009) *Compliance Report: Alcohol Advertising Survey 2009.* London: ASA.

Allemend, M., Steiger, A. E. and Fend, H. A. (2015) Empathy development in adolescence predicts social competencies in adulthood. *Journal of Personality,* 83 (2), 229-241.

Allen, V. (2019) *Statistics for Eating Disorders,* 15 June 2019. [Accessed 3 March 2020]. http//www.dailymail.co.uk

Anderson, C. A. and Dill, K. E. (2000) Video games and aggressive thoughts, feelings, and behaviour in the laboratory and in life. *Journal of Personality and Social Psychology,* 78 (4), 772-790.

Anderson, C. A., Shibuya, A., Ihori N., Swing, E. L., Bushman, B. J., Sakamoto, A., Rothstein, H. R. and Saleem, M. (2010) Violent video game effects on aggression, empathy, and prosocial behavior in eastern and western countries: a meta-analytic review. *Psychological Bulletin,* 136 (2), 151-173.

Anderson, P., De Bruijn, A., Angus, K., Ross, G. and Hastings, G. (2009) Impact of alcohol advertising and media exposure on adolescent alcohol use: A systematic review of longitudinal studies. *Alcohol and Alcoholism,* 44 (3), 229-243.

Atkinson, A., Elliot, G., Bellis, M. and Sumnall, H. (2011) *Young People, Alcohol, and the Media,* [Accessed 27 August 2019]. https://www.ias. org.uk/uploads/pdf/Underage%20 drinking%20docs/young-people-alcohol-mediaEBOOK.pdf.

Back, L., Crabbe, T. & Solomos, J. (2001) *The Changing Face of Football:*

Racism, Identity and Multiculture in the English Game. Oxford: Berg Publishers.

Bandura, A. (1977) *Social Learning Theory.* New York: General Learning Press.

Barak, A. & Dolev-Cohen, M. (2006) Does activity level in online support groups for distressed adolescents determine emotional relief. *Counselling and Psychotherapy Research,* 6, 186-190.

Baumgartner, S. E., Sumter, S. R., Jochen, P. & Valkenburg P. M. (2015) Sexual self-presentation on social network sites: Who does it and how is it perceived? *Computers in Human Behaviour,* 50, 91-100.

Becker, K., Mayer, M., Nagenborg, M., El-Faddagh, M. and Scmidt, M. H. (2014) Parasuicide online: Can suicide websites trigger suicidal behaviour in predisposed adolescents? *Nord J Psychiatry,* 58, 111-114.

Bene, E. (1965) On the genesis of female homosexuality. *The British Journal of Psychiatry,* 111 (478), 815-821.

Benn, S. L. (2017) *The Exploration of Young Audiences and Identity Development Through Social Media Platforms,* Open Access Master's Theses, [Accessed 13 March 2019]. https://digitalcommons.uri.edu/theses.

Benner, A. D. and Graham, S. (2011) Latino adolescents' experiences of discrimination across the first 2 years of high school: Correlates and influences on educational outcomes. *Child Development,* 82 (2), 508-519.

Benner, A. D., Wang, Y., Shenc, Y., Boylea, A. E., Polka, R. and Chenga, Y. (2018) Racial/ethnic discrimination and well-being during adolescence: A meta-analytic review. *American Psychology,* 73 (7), 855-883.

Berkowitz, A. D. (2004) 'An overview of the social norms approach', in Lederman, L. C. and Stewart, L. C. (eds.) *Changing the culture of college drinking: A socially situated prevention campaign.* New York: Hampton Press.

Berkowitz, D., Manohar, N. N., and Tinkler, J. E. (2010) Walk like a man, talk like a woman: teaching the social construction of gender. *Teaching Sociology,* 38, 132-143.

Berne, S., Frisén, A. and Kling, J. (2014) Appearance-related cyberbullying: A qualitative investigation of characteristics, content, reasons, and effects. *Body Image,* 11, 527-533.

Berzonsky, M. D. (2003) Identity style and well-being: Does commitment matter? *Identity,* 3 (2), 231-245.

Beta Cambridge (2020) *Video games are just for kids, and teenage boys, right?!*

[Accessed 25 November 2020]. https://beta.cambridgeenglish.org.

Bobkowski, P. S., Brown, J. D. and Neffa, D. R. (2012) "Hit me up and we can get down" US youths' risk behaviours and sexual disclosure in Myspace profiles. *Journal of Children and Media*, 6 (1), 119-134.

Bonnet, A. (2000) *Anti-Racism*. London: Routledge.

Bonomo, Y., Coffey, C., Wolfe, R., Lynskey, M., Bowes, G. and Patton, G. (2001) Adverse outcomes of alcohol use in adolescents. *Addiction,* 96, (10), 1485-1496.

Boyd, D. M. and Ellison, N. B. (2007) Social network sites: Definition, history, and scholarship. *Journal of Computer-Mediated Communication,* 13 (1), 210-230.

Brechwald, W. A. and Prinstein, M. J. (2011) Beyond Homophily: A Decade of Advances in Understanding Peer Influence Processes. *Journal of Research on Adolescence,* 21, 1, 166-179.

Brittian, A. S., Toomey, R. B., Gonzales, N. A. and Dumka, L. E. (2013) Perceived discrimination, coping strategies, and Mexican origin adolescents' internalizing and externalizing behaviors: Examining the moderating role of gender and cultural orientation. *Applied Developmental Science,* 17, 4-19.

Brown, B. B. and Larson, J. (2009) 'Peer relationships in adolescence', in Lerner, S. M. and Steinberg, L. (eds.) *Handbook of adolescent psychology: Contextual influences on adolescent development.* Hoboken, NJ: John Wiley & Sons, Inc. 74-103.

Brown, C. S. and Bigler, R. S. (2005) Children's perceptions of discrimination: A developmental model. *Child Development,* 76 (3), 533-553.

Brown, R. and Gregg, M. (2012) The pedagogy of regret: Facebook, binge drinking and young women. *Continuum,* 26, 357-369.

Bulman, M. (2018) *Teenage suicides in England and Wales rise by 67% since 2010,* [Accessed 3 January 2021]. https://www.independent.co.uk/news/uk/home-news/teenage-suicides-england-and-wales-2010-ons-a8522331.html.

Burton, K. A., Florell, D. and Wygant, D. B. (2013) The role of peer attachment and normative beliefs about aggression on traditional bullying and cyberbullying. *Psychology in the Schools,* 50, 103-115.

Buss, D. M. and Schmitt, D. P. (1993) Sexual strategies theory: an evolutionary perspective on human mating. *Psychological Review,* 100 (2), 204-232.

Bussey, K. and Bandura, A. (1999) Social cognitive theory of gender development and differentiation. *Psychological Review,* 106 (4), 676-713.

Buzzwell, S. and Rosenthal, D. (1996) Constructing a sexual self: Adolescents' sexual self-perceptions and sexual risk-taking. *Journal of Research on Adolescence,* 6, 489-513.

Cassidy, W., Jackson, M. and Brown, K. N. (2009) Sticks and stones can break my bones, but how can pixels hurt me? Students' experiences with cyber-bullying. *School Psychology International,* [Accessed 22 May 2019]. https://doi.org/10.1177/0143034309106948.

Chalfen, R. (2009) 'It's only a picture': sexting, 'smutty' snapshots and felony charges. *Visual Studies,* 24 (3), 258-268.

Chua, T. H. H. and Chang, L. (2016) Follow me and my beautiful selfies: Singapore teenage girls' engagement in self-presentation and peer comparison on social media. *Computers in Human Behavior,* 55, 190-197.

Collings, S, C., Fortune, S., Steers, D., Currey, N. and Hawton, K. et al. (2011) *Media influences on suicidal behaviour: An interview study of young people in New Zealand. Auckland, New Zealand,* Te Pou o Te Whakaaro Nui, of The National Centre Mental Health Research, Information and Workforce Development.

Coyne, S. (2020) *Is video addiction real?* [Accessed 10 October 2020]. https//: www.sciencedaily.

Crone, E. A. and Konijn, E. A. (2018) Media use and brain development during adolescence. *Nature Communications,* 9 article 588, 1-10.

C. S. Mott Children's Hospital. *Mott Poll Report: Game on: Teens and video games,* [Accessed 21 January 2020]. https:// mottpoll.org/sites/default/files/documents/012020VideoGames.

Daine, K., Hawton, K., Singaravelu, V., Stewart, A., Simkin, S. and Montgomery, P. (2013) *The Power of the Web: A Systematic Review of Studies of the Influence of the Internet on Self-Harm and Suicide in Young People,* [Accessed 24 April 2018]. https://journals.plos.org/plosone/article?id=10.1371/journal.phone. 0077555.

Darwich, L., Hymel, S. and Waterhouse, T. (2012). School avoidance and substance use among lesbian, gay, bisexual and questioning youths: The impact of peer victimization and adult support. *Journal of Educational Psychology,* 104 (2), 381-392.

Davis, K. (2012) Friendship 2.0: Adolescents' experiences of belonging and self-disclosure online. *Journal of Adolescence,* 35, 1527-1536.

De Bellis, M. D., Clark, D. B., Beers, S. R., Soloff, P. H., Boring, A. M., Hall, J., Kersh. A. and Keshaven, M. S. (2000) Hippocampal volume in adolescent-onset alcohol use disorders. *American Journal of Psychiatry,* 157 (5), 737-744.

Definition of Child Abuse, [Accessed 24 May 2020]. https://www.gov.uk/ goverment/ publications, Ref: DFE-00124-2015.

de Freitas, S. (2006) *Learning in Immersive Worlds: A Review of Game-based Learning,* [Accessed 10 January 2021]. https://researchrepository. murdoch.edu.au/id/eprint/35774/1/gamingreport_v3.pdf.

Devit, K. and Roker, D. (2009) The role of mobile phones on family communication. *Children & Society,* 23 (3), 189-202.

Dickens, C. (reprinted 2018) *A Christmas Carol.* Hertfordshire: Wordsworth Editions.

Diliberto, G. M. and Mattey, E. (2009) Sexting: Just how much of a danger is it and what can school nurses do about it? *NASN School Nurse,* 24, 262-267.

Dir, A. L., Coskunpinar, A., Steiner, J. L. and Cyders, M. A. (2013) Understanding differences in sexting behaviors across gender, relationship status, and sexual identity, and the role of expectancies in sexting. *Cyberpsychology, Behavior, and Social Networking,* 16 (8), 568-574.

Duggan, J. M., Heath, N. L., Lewis, S. P. and Baxter, A. L. (2012) An examination of the scope and nature of non-suicidal self-injury online activities: Implications for school mental health professionals. *School Mental Health,* 4, 56-67.

Dunlop, S. M., More, E. and Romer, D. (2011) Where do youth learn about suicides on the Internet, and what influence does this have on suicidal ideation? *The Journal of Child Psychology & Psychiatry,* 52, 1073-1080.

Education Policy Institute (2017) Social Media and children's mental health: a review of the evidence. *EPI,* [Accessed 19 June 2019]. https://epi.org. uk/publications-and-research/social-media-childrens-mental-health-review-evidence.

Elkind, D. (1967) Egocentrism in adolescence. *Child Development,* 38 (4), 1025-1034.

Ellis, S. J. (2015) 'Lesbian psychology', in Richards, C. and John-Barker, M. (eds.) *The Palgrave handbook of the psychology of sexuality and gender.* Basingstoke: Palgrave Macmillan UK.109-128.

Erikson, E. H. (1995) *Identity: Youth and Crises.* New York: Norton & Co.

Farok, N. H. M. and Mahmud, N. (2020) The influence of social media on suicidal ideation: a systematic literature review. *Journal of Research in Psychology*, 2 (1), 4-9.

Ferguson, C. J. and Olson, C. K. (2013) Friends, fun, frustration and fantasy: Child motivations for video game play. *Motivation and Emotion,* 37, 154-164.

Ferguson, C. J., Rueda S., Cruz A., Ferguson D., Fritz S. and Smith, S. (2008) Violent video games and aggression: causal relationship or by product of family violence and intrinsic violence motivation? *Criminal Justice Behaviour,* 31, 2231-2237.

Ferguson C. J., San Miguel C., Garza, A. and Jerabeck, J. M. (2012) A longitudinal test of video game violence influences on dating and aggression: a 3-year longitudinal study of adolescents. *Journal Psychiatric Research,* 46 (2) 141-146.

Fortune, S., Sinclair, J. and Hawton, K. (2008) Adolescents' views on preventing self-harm. *Social Psychiatry and Psychiatric Epidemiology,* 43, 96-104.

Garris, R., Ahlers R. & Driskell, J. (2002) Games, motivation and learning: a research and practice model. *Simulation and Gaming,* 33, 441-467.

Gask, L. (2000) 'Suicide and deliberate self-harm', in Feltham, C. and Horton, I. (eds.) *Handbook of counselling and psychotherapy.* London: Sage. 559-566.

Gillborn, D., Rollock, N., Vincent, C. and Ball, S. J. (2012) "You got a pass, so what more do you want?" Race, class and gender intersections in the educational experiences of the Black middle class. *Race Ethnicity and Education,* 15 (1), 121-139.

Goffman, E. (1990) *The Presentation of Self in Everyday Life.* London: Penguin Books.

Gonzales, A. L. and Hancock, J. T. (2011) Mirror, mirror on my Facebook wall: Effects of exposure to Facebook on self-esteem. *Cyberpsychology, Behavior, and Social Networking,* 14 (1-2), 79-83.

Greitemeyer, T. (2014) Intense acts of violence during video game play make daily life aggression appear innocuous: a new mechanism why violent video games increase aggression. *Journal of Experimental Social Psychology,* 50, 52-56.

Griffin, C., Bengry-Howell, A., Hackley, C., Mistral. W. and Szmigin, I. (2009) 'Every time I do it I absolutely annihilate myself': Loss of (self-) consciousness and loss of memory in young people's drinking narratives. *Sociology,* 43, 457-476.

Gross, R. (2004) *Psychology: The Science of Mind and Behaviour.* London: Hodder & Stoughton. 133.

Guinier, L. (2004) From racial liberalism to racial literacy: Brown v. board of education and the interest-divergence dilemma. *Journal of American History,* 91 (1), 92-118.

Hadid, C. (2015) *Why some 13-year-olds check social media 100 times a day,* [Accessed 13 October 2019]. http://www.cnn.com/2015/10/05/health/being13-teens-social-media-study/.

Harper, G. W., Pedro, A., Serrano, P. A., Bruce, D. and Baumeister, J. A. (2016) The Internet's multiple roles in facilitating the sexual orientation identity development of gay and bisexual male adolescents. *American Journal of Men's Health,* 10 (5), 359-376.

Haw, C., Hawton, K., Niedzwiedz, C. and Platt, S. (2013) Suicide clusters: A review of risk factors and mechanisms. *Suicide Life-Threatening Behavior,* 43, 97-108.

Hawton, K., Saunders, K. E. A. and O'Connor, R. C. (2012) Self-harm and suicide in adolescents. *The Lancet,* 379, (9834), 2373-2382.

Hawton, K. and Williams, K. (2002) Influences of the media on suicide: Researchers, policy makers, and media personnel need to collaborate on guidelines. BM.J, [Accessed 15 January 2019]. https://doi.org/10.1136/bmj.325.7377.1374.

Hay, C. and Meldrum, R. (2010) Bullying victimization and adolescent self-harm: Testing hypotheses from general strain theory. *Journal of Youth and Adolescence,* 39, 446-459.

Heine, S, J., Takemoto, T., Moskalenko, S., and et al. (2008) Mirrors in the head: Cultural variation in objective self-awareness. *Personality & Social Psychology Bulletin,* 34, 879-87.

Hinduja, S. and Patchin, J. W. (2009) Personal information of adolescents on the Internet: A quantitative content analysis of Myspace. *Journal of Adolescence,* 31, 125-146.

Hughes, J, M., Bigler, R, S. and Levy, S.R. (2007) Consequences of learning about historical racism among European American and African American children. *Child Development,* 78, 6, 1689-1705.

Huntermann, N. and Morgan, M. (2001) 'Mass media and identity development', in Singer, D. G. and Singer. J. L. (eds.). *Handbook of children and the media.* Thousand Oaks, California 91320: Sage Publications. 303-320.

Jägermeister Site on YouTube [Accessed 12 May 2020]. https://www.

Jägermeister.com.

Jang, Y. J., Han, K., Shih, P. C. and Dongwon, L. (2015) Generation like: Comparative characteristics in Instagram. *CHI '15: Proceedings of the 33rd Annual ACM Conference on Human Factors in Computing Systems,* 4039-4042, [Accessed 9 September 2019]. https://doi.org/10.1145/2702123.2702555.

Joseph-Salsibury, R. (2020) *Race and Racism in English Secondary Schools.* Runnymede: London.

Kar, S. K., Choudhury, A. and Singh, A. P. (2015) Understanding normal development of adolescent sexuality: A bumpy ride. *Journal of Human Reproductive Sciences,* 8 (2), 70-74.

Kassimeris, C. (2009) Football and prejudice in Belgium and The Netherlands. *Sport in Society,* 12 (10), 1327-1335.

Katsumata, Y., Matsumato, T., Kitani, M. and Takeshima, T. (2008) Electronic media use and suicidal ideation in Japanese adolescents. *Psychiatry and Clinical Neurosciences,* 62, 744-746.

Kim, K. M. (2020) What makes adolescents psychologically distressed? Life events as risk factors for depression and suicide. *European Child and Adolescent Psychiatry,* [Accessed 3 March 2019]. https://doi.org/10.1007/s00787-020-01520-9.

Kim, K., Ryu, E., Chon, M. Y., Yeun, E. J., Choi, S. Y., Seo, J. S. and Nam, B. W. (2006) Internet addiction in Korean adolescents and its relation to depression and suicidal ideation: A questionnaire survey. *International Journal of Nursing Studies,* 43, 185-192.

Kuss, D. J. and Griffiths, M. D. (2012) Internet gaming addiction: A systematic review of empirical research. *International Journal of Mental Health and Addiction,* 10 (2), 278-296.

Lam, L. T., Peng, Z., Mai, J. and Jing, J. (2009) The association between internet addiction and self-injurious behaviour among adolescents. *Injury Prevention,* 15, 403-408.

Lay, K. (2018) *Statistics on Self-Harm,* [Accessed 19 October 2019]. https://www.thetimes.co.uk/article/self-harming-by-teenage-girls-doubles-in-20-years-x2vbzm87m

Laye-Gindu, A. and Schonert-Reichl, K. A. (2005) Nonsuicidal self-harm among community adolescents: Understanding the "whats" and "whys" of self-harm. *Journal of Youth and Adolescence,* 34, 447-457.

Leary, M. R. (1995) *Self-Presentation: Impression Management and Interpersonal Behavior.* Dubuque, JA: Brown & Benchmarks.

Lee-Won, R. J., Shim, M., Joo, K. Y. and Park, S. G. (2014) Who puts the best "face" forward on Facebook? Positive self-presentation in online social networking and the role of self-consciousness, actual-to-total Friends ratio, and culture. *Computers in Human Behavior,* 39, 413-423.

Litt, D. M. and Stock, M. L. (2011). Adolescent alcohol-related risk cognitions: The roles of social norms and social networking sites. *Psychology of Addictive Behaviors,* 25 (4), 708–713.

Litt, E. (2012) Knock, knock. Who's there? The imagined audience. *Journal of Broadcasting & Electronic Media,* 56 (3), 330-345.

Loney, J. (1973) Family dynamics in homosexual women. *Archives of Sexual Behaviour,* 2 (4), 343-350.

Manago, A. M., Graham, M. B., Greenfield, P. M. and Salimkhan, G. (2008) Self-presentation and gender on Myspace, *Journal of Applied Developmental Psychology* 29, 446-458.

Mascheroni, G., Vincent, J. and Jimenez, E. (2015) "Girls are addicted to likes so they post semi-naked selfies": Peer mediation, normativity, and the construction of identity online. *Cyberpsychology: Journal of Psychosocial Research on Cyberspace,* 9 (1), article 5, doi: 10.5817/CP2015-1-5.

Maylor, U., Ross, A., Rollock, N. and Williams, K. (2006) *Black Teachers in London.* London: Mayor of London.

Maylor, U., Smart, S., Kuyok, A. K. and Ross, A. (2009) 'Black children's achievement programme evaluation'. *Institute for Policy Studies in Education, Research Report DCSF-RR177.* London: Department for Children, Schools and Families.

McClean, S. (2016) Alcohol and the constitution of friendship for young adults. *Sociology,* 50, 93-108.

McKown, C. and Weinstein, R. S. (2003) The development and consequences of stereotype consciousness in middle childhood. *Child Development,* 74 (2), 498-515.

Messias, E., Castro, J., Saini, A., Usman, M. and Peeples, D. (2011) Sadness, suicide, and their association with video game and internet overuse among teens: Results from the Youth Risk Behavior Survey 2007 and 2009. *Suicide and Life-Threatening Behavior,* 41, 307-315.

Mikkola, H., Oinas, M., & Kumpulainen, K. (2008). 'Net-based identity and body image among young IRC-Gallery users' in McFerrin, K, Weber, R, Carlsen, R, & Willis, D. (eds.) *Proceedings of SITE 2008--Society for Information Technology & Teacher Education International Conference* (pp. 3080-3085). Las Vegas, Nevada, USA: Association for the

Advancement of Computing in Education (AACE). [Accessed 24 August 2020]. https://www.learntechlib.org/primary/p/27700/.

Mitchell, K, J., Wells, M., Priebe, G. and Ybarra, M. L. (2014) Exposure to websites that encourage self-harm and suicide: Prevalence rates and association with actual thoughts of self-harm and thoughts of suicide in the United States. *Journal of Adolescence,* 37, (8), 1335-1344.

Mitchell, K. J. and Ybarra, M. L. (2007) Online behavior of youth who engage in self-harm provides clues for preventive intervention. *American Journal of Preventative Medicine,* 45, 392-396.

Moran, R. (2000) Racism in football: A victim's perspective. *Soccer & Society,* 1, 190-200.

Moreira, M. T., and Foxcroft, D. (2010) *Social Norms Interventions to Reduce Alcohol Misuse in University or College Students,* (Review) Issue 1. The Cochrane Library.

Moreno, M. A., Briner, L. R., Williams, A., Walker, L. and Christakis, D. A. (2009) "Real use" or "real cool": Adolescents speak out about displayed alcohol references on social networking websites. *Journal of Adolescent Health,* 45 (4), 420-422.

Moreno, M. A., Grant, A., Kacvinsky, L., Egan, K. G. and Fleming, M. F. (2012) College students' alcohol displays on Facebook: Intervention considerations. *Journal of American College Health,* 60 (5), 388-394.

Morgan, E. M., Snelson, C. and Elison-Bowers, P. (2010) Image and video disclosure of substance use on social media websites. *Computers in Human Behavior,* 26 (6), 1405-1411.

Mundt, M. P. (2011) The impact of peer social networks on adolescent alcohol use initiation. *Academic Pediatrics,* 11 (5), 414-421.

Nezleck, J, B., Hampton, G, D. and Shean, G. D. (2000) Clinical depression and day-to-day social interaction in a community sample. *Journal of Abnormal Psychology,* 109 (1), 11-19.

Nitschke, P. and Stewart, F. (2016) *The Peaceful Pill Handbook.* Exit International USA.

Noll, J. G., Shenk, C. E., Barnes, J. E. and Putman, F. (2009) Childhood abuse, avatar choices, and other risk factors associated with Internet-initiated victimization of adolescent girls. *Pediatrics,* 123 (6), e1078-1083. [Accessed 2 February 2019]. https://doi.org/10.1542/peds.2008-2983.

Noom, M, J., Deković, M, and Meeus, W. (2001) Conceptual analysis and measurement of adolescent autonomy. *Journal of Youth and Adolescence,* 30, 577-595.

Oberst, U., Renau, V., Chamarro, A. and Carbonell, X. (2016) Gender stereotypes in Facebook profiles: Are women more female online? *Computers in Human Behavior*, 60, 559-564.

Padilla-Walker, L. M., Nelson, L. J., Carroll, J. S. and Jensen, A. C. (2010) More than just a game: Video game and Internet use during emerging adulthood. *Journal of Youth and Adolescence*, 39, 103-113.

Palmgvist, R. and Santavirta, N. (2006) What friends are for: The Relationship between body image, substance abuse, and peer influence among Finnish adolescents. *The Journal of Youth and Adolescence*, 35 (2), 203-217.

Pingel, E. S., Thomas, L., Harmell, C. and Bauemeister, J. A. (2013) Creating comprehensive, youth centred, culturally, appropriate, sex education: What do young gay, bisexual, and questioning men want? *Sexuality Research and Social Policy*, 10, 293-301.

Prensky, M. (2001) Digital Natives, Digital Immigrants: Part 1. *On the Horizon*, 9, 1-6.

Przybylski, A. K., Murayama, K., DeHaan, C. R. and Gladwell, V. (2013) Motivational, emotional and behavioral correlates of fear of missing out. *Computers in Human Behavior*, 29 (4), 1841-1848.

Quintana, S, M. and McKown, C. (2008) 'Introduction: race, racism, and the developing child', in Quintana, S. M. and Mckown, C. (eds.) *Handbook of race, racism, and the developing child.* Hoboken, NJ, US: John Wiley & Sons Inc.1-15.

Ramsey, G. (1996) Transexuals: *Candid Answers to Private Questions.* Freedom, CA 95019: The Crossing Press.

Reber, A, S. and Reber, E. (2001) *The Penguin Dictionary of Psychology.* London: Penguin Books Ltd.

Ridout, B., Campbell, A. and Ellis, L. (2012) 'Off your Face (book)': Alcohol in online social identity construction and its relation to problem drinking in university students. *Drug and Alcoholic Review*, 31, 20-26.

Ringrose, J. (2011) 'Are you sexy, flirty or a slut? Exploring sexualization on how teen girls perform/negotiate digital sexual identity on social networking sites,' in Gill, R. and Scharff, C. (eds.) *New femininities: Post feminism, neoliberalism and subjectivity.* London: Palgrave. 99-116.

Ringrose, J. (2009) 'Sluts, whores, fat slags and playboy bunnies: teen girls' negotiations of "sexy" on social networking sites and at school', in Jackson, C. & Reynolds, E. (eds*.) Girls and education 3-16: continuing concerns, new agendas.* New York, NY: McGraw Hill Open University

Press.170-172.

Ritchie, S. (2000) 'Eating problems,' in Feltham, C. and Horton, I. (eds.) *Handbook of counselling and psychotherapy.* London: Sage. 461-469.

Rodham, K. and Hawton, K., (2009) 'Epidemiology and phenomenology of nonsuicidal self-injury', in Nock, M. K. (ed) *Understanding nonsuicidal self-injury: Origins, assessment, and treatment.* Washington DC: American Psychological Association, 37-62.

Rosario, M. and Schrimshaw, E. W. (2014) 'Theories and etiologies of sexual orientation,' in Tolman, D. L. and Diamond, L. M. (eds.) *APA handbook of sexuality and psychology.* Washington, DC: American Psychological Association. 556-559.

Rosario, M. E., Schrimshaw, E. W. and Hunter, J. (2011) Different patterns of sexual identity development over time: Implications for the psychological adjustment of lesbian, gay and bisexual youths. *Journal of Sex Research*, 48 (1), 3-15.

Rothon, C., Head, J., Klineberg, E. and Stanfield, S. (2011) Can social support protect bullied adolescents from adverse outcomes? A prospective study on the effects of bullying on the educational achievement and mental health of adolescents at secondary schools in East London. *Journal of Adolescence,* 34 (3), 579-588.

Rubin, J. D. and McClelland, S. I. (2015) Even though it's a small checkbox, it's a big deal: stresses and strains of managing sexual identity (s) on Facebook. *Culture, Health & Sexuality,* 17 (4), 512-526.

Salimkhan, G., Manago, A. M. and Greenfield, P. M. (2010) The construction of the virtual Self on Myspace. *Cyberpsychology: Journal of Psychosocial Research on Cyberspace,* 4 (1), Article 1. [Accessed 7 July 2018]. https://cyberpsychology.eu/article/view/4231.

Sanders-Phillips, K., Settles-Reaves, B., Walker, D. and Brownlow, J. (2019) Social inequality and racial discrimination: Risk factors for health disparities in children of color. *Paediatrics,* 124 (3), 176–186.

Schouten, A. P., Valkenburg, P.M. and Peter. J. (2007) Precursors and underlying processes of adolescents' online self-disclosure: Developing and testing an "Internet-attribute-perception" model. *Media Psychology,* [Accessed 2 January 2020]. https://doi.org/10.1080/15213260701375686.

Shafer, A., Bobkowski, P. and Brown, J. D. (2013) Sexual media practice: 'How adolescents select, engage with, and are affected by sexual media', in Dill, K. E. (ed) *Oxford library of psychology. The Oxford handbook of media psychology.* Oxford University Press. 223-251.

Shao, R. and Wang, Y. (2019) The relation of violent video games to adolescent aggression: An examination of moderated mediation effect. *Frontiers in Psychology,* [Accessed 11 September 2019]. https://doi.org/10.3389/fpsyg.2019.00384.

Siibak, A. (2009) Constructing the self through the photo selection-visual impression management on social networking websites. *Cyberpsychology: Journal of Psychosocial Research on Cyberspace,* 3 (1), Article 1. [Accessed 7 October 2018]. https://cyberpsychology.eu/article/view/4218.

Smithson, J., Sharkey, S., Hewis, E., Jones. R., Emmens, T., Ford, T. and Owens, C. (2011) Problem presentation and responses on an online forum for young people who self-harm. *Discourse Studies,* 13, 487-501.

Spear, L. P. (2002) The adolescent brain and the college drinker: biological basis of propensity to use and misuse alcohol. *Journal of Studies on Alcohol,* Supplement (s14), 71-81.

Status of Mind (2017) [Accessed 19 June 2019]. https://www.rsph.org.uk (2017) our-work › campaigns › status-of-mind.

Steinberg, L. (2007) Risk taking in adolescence: New perspectives from brain and behavioral science. *Current Directions in Psychological Science: Sage Journals,* [Accessed 20 September 2020]. https://doi.org/10.1111/j.1467-8721.2007.00475.x

Stevens, S. (2019) *The Effect of Video Games on Young People's Mental Health,* [Accessed 27 October 2019]. https//www.england.nhs.uk.

Strano, M. M. (2008) User descriptions and interpretations of self-presentation through Facebook profile images. *Cyberpsychology,* 2, 5.

Subrahmanyam, K. P., Greenfield, P., Kraut, R. and Gross, E. (2001) The Impact of Computer Use on Children's and Adolescents' Development. *Applied Developmental Psychology,* 22 (1), 7-30.

Tolman, D. L. (2002) *Dilemma of Desire: Teenage Girls Talk About Sexually.* Cambridge: MA: Harvard University Press.

Trepte, S. and Reinecke, L. (2010) Avatar creation and video game enjoyment: Effects of life-satisfaction, game competitiveness, and identification with the avatar. *Journal of Media Psychology,* 22, 171-184.

Tynes, B. M., Rose, C. A., Hiss, S., Umaña-Taylor, A. J., Mitchell, K. and Williams, D. (2016) Virtual environments, online racial discrimination, and adjustment among a diverse school-based sample of adolescents. *International Journal of Gaming and Computer-Mediated Simulations,* 6 (3), 1-16.

Umaña-Taylor, A. J. (2016) A Post-Racial Society in Which Ethnic-Racial

Discrimination Still Exists and Has Significant Consequences for Youths' Adjustment. *Current Directions in Psychological Science*, 25, 111-118.

Umaña-Taylor, A. J., Quintana, S. M., Lee, R. M., Cross, W. E., Rivas-Drake, D., Schwartz, S. J. and Seaton, E. (2014) Ethnic and racial identity during adolescence and into young adulthood: An integrated conceptualization. *Child Development*, 85, 21-39.

Van Oosten, J. and Vandenbosh, L. (2017) Sexy online self-presentation on social networking sites and their willingness to engage in sexting: A comparison of gender and age. *Journal of Adolescence,* 54, 42-50.

Van Oosten, J, M. F., Peter, J. and Boot, I. (2014) Exploring associations between exposure to sexy online self-presentation and adolescents' sexual attitudes and behavior. *Journal of Youth and Adolescence*, 44, 1078-1091.

Velleman, R. (2009) *Influences on how children and young people learn about and behave towards alcohol: A review of the literature.* York: Joseph Rowntree Foundation.

Wallace, P. (2014) Internet addiction disorder and youth. *EMBO,* Report 15 (1), 12-16.

Walther, J. B. (1996) Computer-mediated communication: Impersonal, interpersonal, and hyperpersonal interaction. *Communication Research,* 23, 3-43.

West, D. J. (2017) *Homosexuality: Its Nature and Causes.* Abingdon, Oxon: Routledge.

Whitehill, J. M., Brockman, L. N. and Moreno, M. A. (2013) "Just talk to me": communicating with college students about depression disclosures on Facebook. *Journal of Adolescent Health,* 52 (1), 122-127.

Whitlock, J. L., Powers, J. L. and Eckenrode, J. (2006) The virtual cutting edge: the internet and adolescent self-injury. *Developmental Psychology,* 42, 407-417.

Winn, J. and Heeter, C. (2009) Gaming, gender, and time: Who makes time to play? *Sex Roles* 61, 1-13.

YMCA (2020) *Young discriminated and Black: the true colour of institutional racism in the UK.* [Accessed 12 November 2020]. https://www.ymca.org.uk.

Young, K. (2009) Understanding online gaming addiction and treatment issues for adolescents. *The American Journal of Family Therapy*, 37, 355-372.

Zhao, S., Grasmuck, S. and Martin, J. (2008) Identity construction on Facebook: Digital empowerment in anchored relationships. *Computers in Human Behaviour,* 24, 1816-1836.

WEBSITES FOR FURTHER SUPPORT

Chapter 3 Bullying and Cyberbullying

The British Association for Counselling and Psychotherapy [Accessed 23 May 2019]. https:// www.bacp.co.uk.
British Psychological Society [Accessed 23 May 2019]. https://www.bps.org.uk.
Bullying UK [Accessed 25 May 2019]. https://www.bullying.co.uk.
National Bullying [Accessed 23 May 2019]. https:/www.nationalbullyinghelpline.co.uk.
NSPCC [Accessed 24 May 2020]. https://www.nspcc.org.uk.
Preventing Bullying [Accessed 27 May 2020]. https:// www. gov.uk.

Chapter 4 Body Image

Beat Eating Disorders [Accessed 12 December 2019]. https://www.beateatingdisorders.org.uk.

Chapter 5 Racism

Show Racism the Red Card [Accessed 28 October 2019]. https://www.theredcard.org.
YMCA [Accessed 12 November 2020]. https://www.ymca.org.uk.

Chapter 6 Sexual Orientation

Coming Out – Advice and Guidance for Parents [Accessed 9 September 2020]. https/www.stonewall.org.uk/help-advice/coming-out/coming-out-advice-and-guidance-parents.

Gender Identity [Accessed 9 September 2020]. https://youngminds.org.uk/
    find-help/for-parents/parents-guide-to-support-gender-identity-issues/.

MESMAC [Accessed 5 June 2020]. https:// www.mesmac.co.uk.

Sexual Health for Gay and Bisexual Men [Accessed 9 September 2020].
    https://www.nhs.uk/live-well/sexual-health/sexual-health-for-gay-and-
    bisexual-men.

Sexual Health for Lesbians and Bisexual Women [Accessed 9 September
    2020]. https://www.nhs.uk/live-well/sexual-health/sexual-health-for-
    lesbian-and-bisexual-women.

Chapter 7 Sexuality

Sexting: What Parents Need to Know [Accessed 27 May 2020]. https://
    kidshealth.org/en/parents/2011-sexting.html.

Chapter 8 Alcohol

Drinkaware [Accessed 5 May 2020] https://www.drinkaware.co.uk.

Frank [Accessed 5 May 2020]. https:// www.talktofrank.com.

Guidelines for the alcohol consumption of children and young people
    [Accessed 14 May 2020]. https://www.gov.uk/government/consultations/
    alcohol-strategy-consultation

Chapter 9 Suicide and Self-Harm

British Association for Counselling and Psychotherapy. [Accessed 23 May
    2019]. https://www.bacp.co.uk.

Cruse Bereavement Care [Accessed 5 February 2020]. https://www.cruse.
    org.uk.

Help for Suicidal Thoughts [Accessed 10 February 2020]. https://www.nhs.
    uk/conditions/suicide/.

Mind for Better Mental Health [Accessed 10 February 2020]. https:// www.
    mind.org.uk.

Prevention of Young Suicide [Accessed 1 March 2020]. https:// www.
    papyrus-uk.org.

Samaritans [Accessed 1 March 2020]. http:// www.samaritans.org.

Where to Get Help for Self-Harm [Accessed 10 February 2020]. https:// www.nhs.uk/conditions/self-harm/.

Young Minds [Accessed 1 March 2020]. https://youngminds.org.uk.

Chapter 10 Games

Behaviour and Discipline in Schools. [Accessed 5 December 2020]. https:// www.gov.uk/government/publications/behaviour-and-discipline-in-schools.

World Health Organisation [Accessed 28 February 2020]. https//www.who. int.

INDEX

During her career Dr Steph Adam has worked extensively with adolescents' mental health because she has a particular interest in providing support and advice to this age group. Her second publication *The Effect of Social Media on Adolescents' Mental Health and Well-Being* is the result of three years research into why young people are so engrossed in social media. Steph explains how today's young people think and behave in a world where social media is featured heavily. She then describes the benefits and risks that may occur, along with advice how parents and teachers can keep their young people safer online.

Steph was awarded a Doctorate degree after successfully completing her research into dream interpretation, and how using dream analysis may promote personal growth. In 2018 she published *The Dream Interpreters: Which One or None?* her first book, which was written for readers to interpret their own dreams without the need for therapy.

Steph currently lives in York. She loves travelling both in the UK and abroad, is a country music fan, and is learning to dance the Margaret Morris method of dance, as well as enjoying socialising with family and friends. To relax, Steph reads Scandi-noir crime novels by authors such as Jo Nesbo and Camilla Läckberg. You can find out more about Steph by visiting her website www.stephadam.co.uk, or you can contact her at https://www.facebook.com/StephAdamAuthor, or https://twitter.com/stephadamauthor.